INTERNATIONAL SERIES OF MONOGRAPHS IN
ANALYTICAL CHEMISTRY

GENERAL EDITORS: R. BELCHER AND H. FREISER

VOLUME 53

PHOTOELECTRON SPECTROSCOPY

Chemical and Analytical Aspects

PHOTOELECTRON SPECTROSCOPY

CHEMICAL AND ANALYTICAL ASPECTS

A. D. BAKER
Queens College, City University of New York

and

D. BETTERIDGE
University College of Swansea, Wales

PERGAMON PRESS

OXFORD · NEW YORK · TORONTO
SYDNEY · BRAUNSCHWEIG

Pergamon Press Ltd., Headington Hill Hall, Oxford

Pergamon Press Inc., Maxwell House, Fairview Park, Elmsford,
New York 10523

Pergamon of Canada Ltd., 207 Queen's Quay West, Toronto 1

Pergamon Press (Aust.) Pty. Ltd., 19a Boundary Street,
Rushcutters Bay, N.S.W. 2011, Australia

Vieweg & Sohn GmbH, Burgplatz 1, Braunschweig

First edition 1972

Library of Congress Catalog Card No. 72–77503

Printed in Great Britain by A. Wheaton & Co., Exeter
08   016910   4

CONTENTS

PREFACE

PHOTOELECTRON spectroscopy has, within the past few years, become one of the most rapidly growing areas in chemistry. At the present time, more publications on the subject often appear within a couple of months than did over the whole of the period 1962–7. This has partly been due to the availability of commercial instruments since 1967, and to a growing recognition that electron spectroscopic techniques have widespread applications throughout chemistry and related sciences.

The authors of this book first worked together in 1968 when a grant from the Agricultural Research Council (U.K.) enabled one of the first batch of commercial photoelectron spectrometers to be set up at the University College of Swansea in order to study the applicability of photoelectron spectroscopy to the analysis of pesticides etc. One of the authors (D. B.) was at that time a lecturer in Analytical Chemistry at Swansea, and he was joined by the other author (A. D. B.) who came to Swansea as a Research Fellow from Oxford, where he had worked in the very early days of photoelectron spectroscopy as a student of Dr. D. W. Turner.

We hope that this book, which represents a balance of the interests of the two authors, provides a readable introduction to the principles of the technique, and its applications in structural and analytical chemistry. We are convinced that the method is of fundamental importance to chemists, and that many are at present put off the subject by the theoretical treatments which are a staple ingredient of most papers in the field. Our emphasis is on the business of obtaining spectra and on interpreting them without recourse to rigorous theoretical methods. We deal with both X-ray (ESCA) and UV-photoelectron spectroscopy (PES).

We are indebted to our colleagues in Swansea, and elsewhere, for their help and for making many valuable suggestions. In particular, we would like to thank Drs. M. Thompson, N. R. Kemp, R. E. Kirby and Mr. C. W. Haigh. We are also especially indebted to Mr. K. Francis, of the Graphic Arts Department, University College of Swansea, for helping to prepare many of the diagrams. Finally, we would like to thank the Agricultural Research Council (U.K.) for providing the funds to initiate a project in photoelectron spectroscopy.

Unless otherwise stated, the UVPE spectra have been drawn from our own work and the X-ray PE spectra from Siegbahn's.

CHAPTER 1

BASIC PRINCIPLES

INTRODUCTION

One of the fundamental concepts of chemistry is that the extra-nuclear electrons of atoms and molecules exist in orbitals of well-defined energies. The technique of electron spectroscopy enables the different binding energies or ionization potentials (IPs) of electrons in different orbitals to be measured. We can refer to these values as the different "orbital ionization potentials".

Electron spectroscopy has proved to be the first experimental technique to provide, for a given atom or molecule, a complete set of orbital ionization potentials, from the valence electrons down to the K-shell electrons. Because these orbital IPs are characteristic features of the parent atom or molecule, electron spectroscopy affords a possible means of compound identification, as well as providing data which has had a profound affect on theoretical chemistry. It is a straightforward technique, which consists essentially of measuring the energy spectrum of the electrons ejected from a sample on bombardment with (usually) monoenergetic rays or particles. The energies of the ejected electrons differ according to their orbitals of origin, and may be related simply to the different orbital ionization potentials of the sample atom or molecule.

The recorded spectrum may thus serve to identify the elements present and/or provide information about the structure of the sample. For example, the K-shell ionization potentials for the first eighteen elements of the Periodic Table vary in a distinctive manner from

1

TABLE 1.1. APPROXIMATE BINDING ENERGIES (eV) FOR THE ELEMENTS OF
THE FIRST AND SECOND ROWS OF THE PERIODIC TABLE*

H 14							He 25
Li 50	Be 110	B 190	C 280	N 400	O 530	F 690	Ne 867
Na 1070	Mg 1305	Al 1560	Si 1840	P 2150	S 2470	Cl 2823	Ar 3203

*More values are given in Appendix 1.

14 eV to 3203 eV (Table 1.1). An experimentally found ionization potential within a few volts of 400 would therefore indicate the presence of nitrogen in the sample, and the extent by which the IP differed from 400 eV, the "chemical shift", would give a clue to the molecular environment of the nitrogen atom, e.g. whether it were in a nitro-group or an amino-group. If there were two peaks of equal area close to 400 eV, it would indicate the presence of two nitrogen atoms in the molecule in non-equivalent positions. IPs in the range 5–30 eV relate to electrons in the valence shell, and the information obtained from this part of the spectrum is concerned with molecular bonding, with substituent effects, and with isomeric and steric changes.

The information to be obtained from electron spectroscopy is unique, although at this stage in its development, in which structural and electronic interpretations are inevitably compared with similar information given by established techniques, its uniqueness is not always emphasized. It is potentially a sensitive method, applicable to a wide range of compounds, and able to give information about all the atoms within a molecule. It is probable that it will become an important analytical method for qualitative, and possibly quantitative analysis.

This monograph aims to deal with the basic principles of instrumentation, and to show how the spectra may provide analytically valuable information.

GENERAL APPARATUS

The basic requirements of an electron spectrometer may be summarized as follows:

(a) Pumping equipment capable of evacuating the apparatus to about 1×10^{-6} mm mercury pressure.

(b) A source of ionizing rays or particles.

(c) A collision chamber into which the ionizing species and the material under investigation can be introduced, and from which electrons may pass into an electron energy analyser.

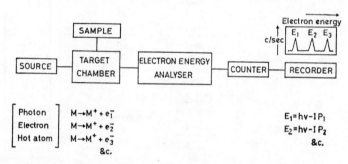

FIG. 1.1. Block diagram showing the arrangement of some of the principle parts of an electron spectrometer. Electrons e_1, e_2, e_3, etc., are ejected from various orbitals of M, with energies E_1, E_2, E_3, etc. The electron spectrum shows the relative numbers of electrons ejected over the possible energy range.

(d) A sampling system by which the appropriate amount of sample in the appropriate physical state can be introduced into the collision chamber.

(e) An electron energy analyser to monitor the electron flux emerging from the collision chamber.

(f) Counting and recording equipment to plot the spectrum.

A block diagram illustrating the arrangement of some of the principle parts is given in Fig. 1.1. In the usual type of investigation, monoenergetic ionizing rays or particles generated in the source are directed onto sample molecules in the target chamber. An electron can then be expelled from any orbital for which the associated ionization potential is less than the energy of the impacting species.

Every ejected electron will possess a quantity of kinetic energy, E, which will be approximately equal in magnitude to the difference between the energy, U, imparted by the impacting species, and the appropriate orbital ionization potential, I:

$$E = U - I. \tag{1.1}$$

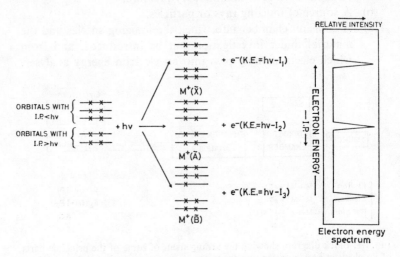

FIG.1.2. Schematic representation of the processes represented by an electron spectrum. On left: molecule with 5 filled levels, 3 of which are acessible to the photons. In the middle: the molecular ions $M^+(\tilde{X})$, $M^+(\tilde{A})$ and $M^+(\tilde{B})$ resulting from ionization from 3 highest occupied orbitals. On right: PE spectrum reflecting MO levels.

In the case where the impacting species is a photon of frequency, ν, U is equal to $h\nu$ where h is Planck's constant, and

$$E = h\nu - I. \tag{1.2}$$

Since the impacting species are directed into an array of identical molecules in an electron spectrometer, electrons can be ejected from all the accessible orbitals (i.e. all those for which $U \geqslant I$). Groups of different energy electrons are thus emitted. All electrons ejected within the solid angle of acceptance of a slit within the target chamber then enter the focusing electron analyser through this slit.

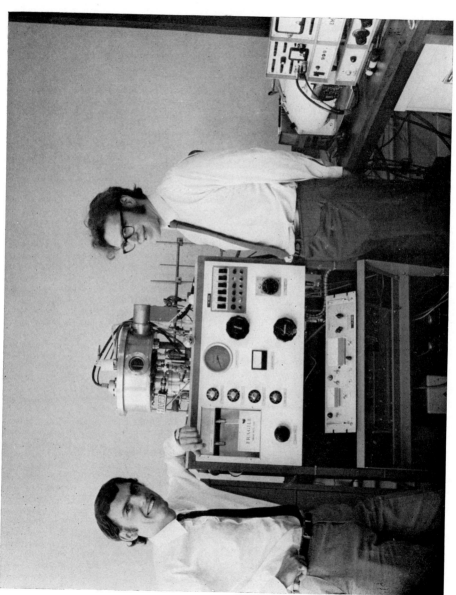

Fig. 1.3. Prototype UV-photoelectron spectrometer marketed by Perkin-Elmer.

Once inside the analyser, the electrons describe different paths depending upon their energies and the voltage applied to the analyser plates. For a given applied voltage, only electrons of one specific energy can be focused onto the exit slit of the analyser. To record a spectrum, the voltage on the analyser plates is swept so that progressively less energetic electrons come to a focus in turn on the exit slit, through which they can pass, be detected, and displayed as bands on chart paper. In this way, a "spectrum" of the kinetic energies of the ejected electrons is obtained. Every peak or

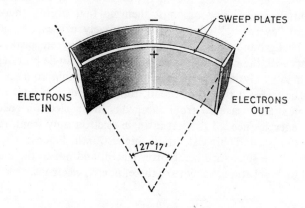

FIG. 1.4. A 127° electrostatic energy analyser. An energy spectrum is obtained by sweeping the voltage on the plates.

band within the spectrum relates to one of the groups of ejected electrons, and therefore to one of the occupied orbitals of the parent substance. The processes which give rise to peaks in an electron spectrum are illustrated schematically in Figs. 1.1 and 1.2. A general view of one type of electron spectrometer is shown in Fig. 1.3, and the focusing electron energy analyser used in this spectrometer is illustrated schematically in Fig. 1.4.

The spectrum as obtained on chart paper consists essentially of the count-rate registered by the focused electrons plotted against the voltage on the analyser electrodes. The voltage needed to focus an electron is clearly related to its kinetic energy, and thus to the parent ionization potential. For easy comparison of spectra obtained from different types of instruments, the x-axis of published spectra is normally calibrated in terms of "orbital ionization potential" expressed in electron volts (eV). One electron volt is numerically equal to 96·3 kJ mole^{-1}.

Multiple ionizations of the sort defined by equation (1.3) can occur

$$M + h\nu = M^{n+} + ne^- \tag{1.3}$$

but the ejected electrons do not give rise to discrete peaks in the spectrum. This is because the energy carried off by the n electrons is randomly partitioned amongst them so that overall there is a statistical "averaging" effect which effectively causes an increase in the background count to the spectrum of discrete peaks. This contrasts with the normal case ($n = 1$) when the single photoejected electron can only have one discrete energy. In this connection, it should be stressed that the second, third, nth, etc., orbital ionization potentials measured from the peaks in an electron spectrum are the energies needed to eject a single electron only from, respectively, the second highest, third highest, nth highest occupied orbitals of the substance being investigated, and not to the energies needed to expel respectively two, three, n, etc., electrons.

CHAPTER 2

FACTORS UNDERLYING INSTRUMENTATION AND THEIR BEARING ON THE INTERPRETATION OF RESULTS

SOURCES

(A) THE DIFFERENT TYPES OF SOURCES

The amount of energy needed to eject an electron from its parent orbital can vary from 5 to 30 eV, for valence-shell electrons, to several hundred or thousand eV for K-shell core electrons. Thus the prime requirement of the source is that it can provide monoenergetic energy within or in excess of this range. In principle a number of different sources, including electrons, photons, metastable atoms, etc., can be used. The manner by which the energy of the bombarding species is transferred to the target molecules varies with the type of source used, and this affects the instrumentation of the spectrometer and the interpretation of the results.

Spectra resulting from photon impact are the easiest to obtain and interpret and have accordingly found the widest application. Most of this book will in fact be concerned with photon-impact-induced spectra ("photoelectron spectra") but first, the other types of spectra, and their relation to each other and to photoelectron spectra, will be noted.

Electrons may be used as a source, but this gives rise to several problems. Firstly, there is the difficulty in generating a sufficiently intense monoenergetic supply.† Electrons emitted from a heated filament have a distribution of velocities and therefore of energies, and an electron lens has to be used to select only those electrons whose velocities lie within a chosen energy span.[1–3]‡ Secondly, more sophisticated ancillary counting equipment is required in order to differentiate primary bombarding electrons from those ejected from sample molecules, and thereby obtain a spectrum whose peaks can be simply related to orbital IPs. The main reason for this is that when one of the primary electrons scores a "hit" on a sample molecule, it does not give up all its energy, E_p, to the molecule (as a photon could), but is scattered with a lower energy, E_s. The difference between the primary and the scattered electron energies ($E_p - E_s$) is transferred to the molecule and can be used to expel an electron from one of the bound orbitals with a kinetic energy equal to ($E_p - E_s - I$) where I is the appropriate orbital ionization potential. Thus to examine the kinetic energy spectrum of only the ejected electrons would be of little use because ($E_p - E_s$) could assume any value, implying that electrons ejected from corresponding orbitals in different molecules of the same sample could have widely different kinetic energies. If the scattered primary electrons and the ejected electrons are examined together, meaningful results can be obtained.

The experimentation then requires coincidence counting techniques so that one examines only electrons ejected from sample molecules which have accepted a chosen specific amount of energy from the primary electrons. In practice, this requires the scattered and the ejected electrons to be sent into different energy analysers linked in a coincidence circuit. This type of approach was suggested independently by both atomic physicists and photoelectron spectroscopists,[4,5] but has only recently reached the experimental stage.[6] The practical problems are considerable, but if they can be overcome, this method of obtaining spectra could have a number of advantages since in principle the source can easily be varied in energy over a very wide range (impossible with photon sources).

---

†Polyenergetic electron beams are suitable for exciting Auger electron spectra (Chapter 7), since Auger electron energies are independent of the incident ionizing energy.

‡References are given at the end of each chapter.

The use of metastable or "hot" atoms as the energizing source for electron spectroscopy has been more widespread than the use of electrons, but is of more interest to the student of collision phenomena than to the analyst. The overall equation for the ionization process brought about by a metastable (often known as "Penning ionization") is

$$A^* + B \to A + B^+ + e^-. \tag{2.1}$$

The reaction does pass through a compound state (A^*B), however, and because of this Penning ionization spectroscopy can reveal information about processes not detected by photoelectron spectroscopy. Results from Penning ionization spectroscopy are described in a series of papers by Cermak and associates.[7-11]

Energies above the six or so electron volts needed to eject electrons from molecules correspond to photon wavelengths in the vacuum ultraviolet† (VUV) part of the electromagnetic spectrum. Siegbahn and his associates in Uppsala, Sweden were the first to investigate the use of K_α X-ray photon sources as sources for electron spectroscopy[12] whilst Turner and others in England[13] and Terenin and others in the Soviet Union[14] pioneered the use of VUV photons. The more energetic X-ray photons used by the Swedish workers enabled them to observe the results of electron emission from both the core and the valence shell orbitals of atoms and molecules, whilst the English group were limited by the VUV photon energies to just the valence shell. However, the diminished natural width of VUV photon band widths as compared with the X-ray photon band widths meant that spectra excited by using the former were much better defined, and allowed fine structure to be resolved.‡ The two approaches are thus complementary. The X-ray photoelectron work, also named "ESCA" (electron spectroscopy for chemical analysis) is usually useful only for the core electrons, whilst the VUV photon work ("PES"—photoelectron spectroscopy) is useful for only the valence-shell electrons. The broader-bands appearing

†The vacuum ultraviolet encompasses the wavelength range from about 2A up to about 2000A. It is known as the "vacuum" ultraviolet because the atmospheric gases (and most other substances) have strong absorption bands in this region, and consequently have to be removed from instruments before measurements can be made.

‡The origin of this structure will be discussed in succeeding pages.

in X-ray excited spectra are usually not too serious a problem for the examination of core orbitals, since these generally have widely differing IPs, but are a great disadvantage for the examination of valence orbitals, because even in a typical simple compound (e.g. a monosubstituted benzene) ten or more valence orbitals are found to have IPs within a 10-eV span, and this many orbitals in so small a range would be indistinguishable as separate features in an X-ray excited spectrum.

(B) SOURCE ENERGIES

Electron spectroscopy normally requires a monoenergetic source. The provision of such a source presents a number of problems. Photons need to have a wavelength of *ca.* 1200 A, or preferably less, to be of any practical importance for photoelectron spectroscopy. Short-wavelength photons can be generated in discharge lamps or in X-ray lamps, but most lamps of these types produce photons of many different wavelengths.[15,16] A grating monochromator[15,16] can nevertheless be used to select photons of only a chosen energy from such a source, an approach which has been used in UV-photoelectron spectroscopy,[17,24]† but there is then an appreciable loss of intensity at the grating, which makes instrumentation difficult. Some lamps, however, produce nearly monoenergetic radiation in the VUV or XUV (X-ray ultraviolet) regions, and this radiation is often used undispersed as a source for electron spectroscopy. There are at present only two VUV monoenergetic sources which are really suitable for use in electron spectroscopy. These depend upon glow discharges in low-pressure ($< 200 \mu$) helium or helium/ hydrogen mixture which generate respectively 584 A (21·2 eV) and 1215 A (10·2 eV) photons, plus other minority emissions which are of such low relative intensities as to be usually unimportant.‡ The helium lamp worked at higher voltages and lower pressures than those suitable for exciting 584 A emission generates up to 70% He(II) emission at 304 A.

†Hewlett-Packard are now manufacturing an X-ray photoelectron spectrometer incorporating a monochromator.

‡Some VUV lamps producing doublet emission lines have also been used in photoelectron spectrometry (see Table 2.1).

Differential pumping of the lamp and target regions is usually employed when undispersed radiation from a glow discharge lamp is used, because of the lack of suitable window materials for passing photons with these wavelengths. A conventional set-up is shown schematically in Fig. 2.1. The discharge takes place in the upper

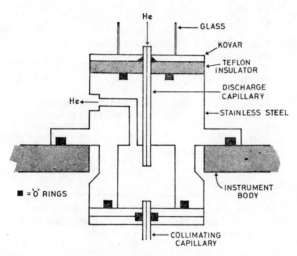

FIG. 2.1. Diagram showing the gas discharge lamp assembly used in a photoelectron spectrometer (see text).

capillary tube, the majority of the light source gas then being evacuated through the pumping line shown. Photons pass on down the lower capillary tube into the target chamber.

Conventional X-ray tubes providing the K_α emission lines of metals have also been used as "monoenergetic" sources for photoelectron spectroscopy. In such experiments a thin "window" (aluminium) has commonly been used to separate the source and ionization chamber compartments. A cold cathode X-ray source claimed to be suitable for windowless operation in electron spectrometry has also been described.[25] The energies of the commonly used XUV, VUV, and metastable atom sources used in electron spectrometry are summarized in Table 2.1.

TABLE 2.1. MONOENERGETIC SOURCES OF ENERGY USED FOR
ELECTRON SPECTROSCOPY

X-ray photon sources	Energy (eV)
Mg K_α	1253·6
Al K_α	1486·6
Na K_α	1041·0
Ag K_α	22,162·9
Cu K_α	8048
Cr K_α	5415
Mo K_α	17,479·3
VUV photon sources	
He(I)	21·2
He(II)	40·8
Lyman α	10·2
Ne(I)	16·65, 16·83 (doublet)†
Ar(I)	11·62, 11·83 (doublet)†
Xe(I)	9·55, 8·42 (doublet)†
Kr(I)	10·02, 10·63 (doublet)†
Metastable atom sources	
He 2¹S	20·61
2³S	19·81

†The use of sources producing doublet emission lines is
rather unsatisfactory because of the resulting doubling of
every feature within an electron spectrum.

Although the radiation emerging from an X-ray tube does contain
components of more than the nominal K_α-wavelengths shown in
the Table 2.1, filter combinations can be used to remove un-
wanted emissions. Minority VUV emissions cannot readily be
filtered out from VUV lamps except perhaps by gas filters. Failure
to recognize the presence of these minority emissions, and also
emissions due to impurities in the lamp, have caused the misinterpre-
tation of some spectra.[19,26-28] Therefore we have listed, in Table
2.2, the wavelengths of the major and the minority emission lines
commonly associated with the various rare gas resonance lamps used
in photoelectron spectroscopy.

Bands caused by impurity or weak intensity lines in the source
will normally be of low intensity, of course, and readily analysed
for what they are. Problems can arise, however, when the ratio of
the ionization cross-section at the minority line wavelength to that

TABLE 2.2. MINORITY EMISSION LINES FREQUENTLY PRESENT IN UNDISPERSED RADIATION FROM SOME TYPICAL UV LAMPS USED IN ELECTRON SPECTROMETRY

Lamp		Emission lines† (A)			
He lamp (untrapped)‡	He lines	237, 243, 304 (2%) 537 (5%)	256 (0·1%) 522 (2%) 584 (100%)		
	Impurity lines	793 (0·5%) 989 (2%) 950 (1%) 1025 (3%) 1134 (5%)	878 (1%) 1304 (3%) 973 (2%) 1215 (9%) 1200 (3%)	O H N	(I) (I) (I)
He lamp (trapped)‡	He lines	304 (2%) 537 (1·7%)	523 (0·2%) 584 (100%)		
	Impurity lines	1025 (0·5%)	1215 (0·5%)		
Argon/helium lamp	Ar lines	543 (1%) 670 (2%) 740 (2%) 932 (5%) 1067 (52%)	582 (1%) 724 (2%) 920 (9%) 1048 (100%)		
	Impurity lines	878 (2%) 1134 (4%) 1025 (4%)	1304 (4%) 1200 (3%) 1215 (35%)		
Neon lamp		No detailed figures, but 1215–A and 1034–A lines are troublesome			

†Line intensities are quoted in parentheses as percentages of the highest intensity emission lines (100%) in each case. The figures given may show small differences from lamp to lamp, and stringent purification can largely eliminate impurity lines.

‡The trap is a tube, packed with charcoal and cooled with liquid nitrogen placed in the helium inlet tube.

at the main line wavelength is appreciable, for then the impurity or satellite bands can assume the same sort of intensity as the main bands in the spectrum. Such an effect resulted in the photoelectron spectrum of mercury being misinterpreted,[26] but fortunately the combination of factors likely to result in a false identification is a rare occurrence.

(C) THE WIDTH OF PHOTON EMISSION LINES

The idea that the exciting photon is truly monoenergetic is in fact unrealistic because there is, in actuality, a distribution of light intensity over a wavelength range, with a maximum at the wavelength value quoted as the "wavelength" of that radiation, and tailing off to zero on either side of the maximum. The width of an emission line will have a considerable bearing upon any spectroscopic measurements carried out using that line. Thus in photoelectron spectroscopy, the width of peaks in the electron kinetic energy spectrum can obviously not be less than the exciting line width.[29,30]

There are a number of factors which can contribute to emission line widths, some of which are the natural width, pressure effects, the Stark effect, self-reversal effects, Doppler effect, and self-absorption effects. Rigorous treatments of these phenomena are given elsewhere,[31,32] but a brief outline is given below with special reference to the production of 584 A emission. Samson has also developed this same theme elsewhere.[33]

(i) *Natural widths* ($\delta\lambda_n$)

Radiation from a discharge lamp stems from transitions from an excited state of some species in the lamp to a state of lower energy. The width of a given spectral line therefore depends upon the mean lifetime, τ, of the excited state. The width of the line due to this factor, free of all other broadening phenomena (see below), is known as the "natural width" and can be represented by:

$$\delta\lambda_n = \frac{\lambda^2}{2\pi c\tau} \tag{2.2}$$

where λ is the nominal wavelength, c is the velocity of light, and $\delta\lambda_n$ is the width of the emission line profile at half its maximum height, i.e. its "half-width". This half-width will thus rise steeply as the wavelength increases, and as the lifetime of the excited state decreases. For the 584 A emission, $\delta\lambda_n = 3 \cdot 3 \times 10^{-5}$ A.

(ii) *Pressure, resonance or Lorentz width* ($\delta\lambda_r$)

The likelihood of an excited atom in the discharge lamp colliding with a "cold" or unexcited atom increases as the pressure increases.

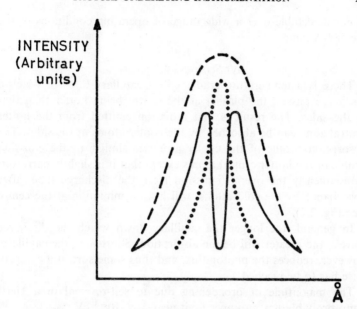

FIG. 2.2. Schematic representation of the effects of self-reversal in a gas discharge resonance lamp. Continuous line, total emission; broken line, emission profile of atoms in centre; dotted line, absorption profile of atoms at sides (cf. ref. 33).

Such a collision shortens τ, and as the equilibrium between ground and excited states is perturbed several changes in the emission line profile take place: (a) the peak is broadened, (b) the maximum of the peak is shifted, and (c) the line profile becomes asymmetric. Point (a) is explained by the simple Lorentz theory which predicts for a He 584-A lamp (584 A comprises *ca.* 98% of the total emission) that $\delta\lambda_r$ is approximately 7.5×10^{-6} A torr^{-1}. The effects of a shift of the wavelength maximum and of asymmetry in the line profile are insignificant in comparison with other effects.

(iii) *The Stark effect*

In principle the electric fields set up by the motion of electrons and ions in the discharge lamp could cause a splitting of the major emission line, but Samson[33] has shown that in practice the effect is not detectable over a wide range of operating conditions of the He 584-A lamp.

(iv) *Self-reversal effects*

There is a temperature gradient in a capillary through which a discharge passes, the plasma at the centre being hotter than that at the sides. The result is that radiation emitted from the hotter central zone can be absorbed by the cooler atoms at the sides. The absorption profile of the cooler atoms is similar to the emission profile of the hotter central atoms except that it is slightly narrower. Consequently the overall emission from the discharge tube, after absorbance by the cold atoms, will have a minimum at the centre (see Fig. 2.2).

In general, the longer the capillary down which the discharge travels, the greater will be the absorption. Shortening the capillary, however, reduces the photon flux, and thus some sort of a compromise has to be reached.

The magnitude of broadening due to self-reversal in a He(I) lamp probably has an upper limit near 5×10^{-3} eV.

(v) *Doppler width* $(\delta\lambda_D)$

The atoms in a discharge have an effective velocity in a definite direction, this velocity being sufficiently great to cause a characteristic Doppler shift in the emitted radiation, given by

$$\delta\lambda_D = 1 \cdot 67 \left(\frac{\lambda}{c}\right) \left(\frac{2RT}{M}\right)^{\frac{1}{2}}. \tag{2.3}$$

The absolute value of the Doppler broadening at 300°K is quite small, e.g. for the 584-A discharge lamp $\delta\lambda_D = 3 \cdot 6 \times 10^{-3}$ A.

(vi) *Self-absorption effects*

In general, photons emerging from the end of a discharge capillary have to traverse a considerable length of "cold gas" before they enter into the system under investigation. Thus in the photoelectron spectrometer set-up illustrated in Fig. 2.1 photons have to pass through "cold helium" which can absorb part of the flux before the photon beam enters the target chamber. Furthermore, only collisions between photons and sample gas molecules taking place in the vicinity of the target chamber slit contribute to the recorded photoelectron flux, and thus all photons absorbed by gas molecules above the slit are wasted. It therefore follows that the target chamber collision zone should be as close as possible to the end of the discharge tube. Some separation between target chamber and lamp is necessary, however, to prevent sample gas entering the lamp, and thus once more some sort of compromise has to be reached.[33] Self-absorption can be minimized by working the lamp at low pressures, and by effective exhaustion of the lamp gas when it emerges from the discharge capillary.

Taking all the above factors into consideration, Samson[33] recommends a capillary of approximately 3 cm, and notes that the diameter does not appear to influence the width of the resonance line.

SAMPLE INTRODUCTION

(A) UV PHOTOELECTRON SPECTROMETERS

A simplified diagram of a VUV photoelectron spectrometer showing the arrangement of the pumping, sample, and light source gas injection lines is shown in Fig. 2.3. The sample may be a gas, liquid, or solid provided that its vapour may be introduced into the target chamber at a pressure between 1 and 150 microns. Once inside the target chamber, vapour can leak away slowly through the exit slit into the analyser compartment, from which it is pumped away. Thus, to maintain a steady pressure, sample is continually leaked into the target chamber during the period over which a spectrum is being run. The Pirani gauge on the collision chamber side of the fine control inlet valve reveals when a "steady-state" condition is obtained. Although the pressure in the ionization chamber may be as high as 150 microns, the pressure within the chamber containing the analyser is maintained below 10^{-4} torr by the pumps, thus enabling the electron-multiplier detector (see below) to work efficiently.

At present there has been no full study of the minimum sample size and of ways in which the sampling system could be improved.

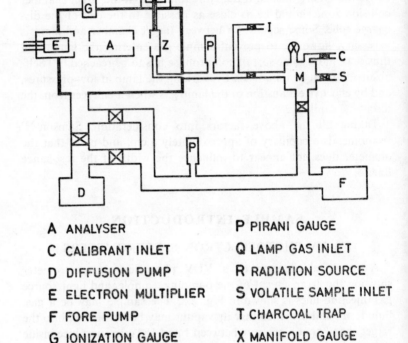

A ANALYSER   P PIRANI GAUGE
C CALIBRANT INLET   Q LAMP GAS INLET
D DIFFUSION PUMP   R RADIATION SOURCE
E ELECTRON MULTIPLIER   S VOLATILE SAMPLE INLET
F FORE PUMP   T CHARCOAL TRAP
G IONIZATION GAUGE   X MANIFOLD GAUGE
I INVOLATILE SAMPLE INLET   Y LAMP OUTLET TO PUMP
M MANIFOLD   Z COLLISION CHAMBER

Fig. 2.3. Schematic diagram of a VUV photoelectron spectrometer.

During our preliminary studies we have obtained good spectra on less than 1 mg of acetone. We have also noted that it is possible for a sample to be adsorbed onto the walls of the tubing connecting the sample and target chamber despite prolonged pumping out. It can then react with the next sample either chemically or simply as a solvent so that the effective concentration is reduced. It is possible to overcome these difficulties by use of a direct inlet probe, but with this a volatile sample is lost too quickly for a spectrum to be obtained and if the vapour pressure of an non-volatile sample is increased by heating the probe, the sample will be deposited in the colder parts of the apparatus where it may well be a nuisance. These problems are interrelated with those of baking the apparatus, improving sensitivity and resolution of the instrument so that spectra may be run more rapidly. A legitimate aim is to introduce samples

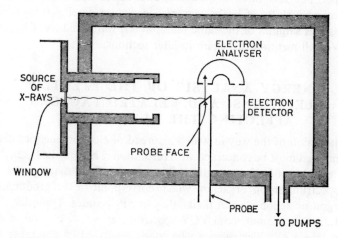

FIG. 2.4. Schematic diagram of an X-ray photoelectron spectrometer with probe for solid samples (see text).

from a GLC column but much further development work will be required before that becomes a routine operation.

(B) X-RAY PHOTOELECTRON SPECTROMETERS

Samples have generally been examined in the solid phase in X-ray photoelectron experiments, although gaseous studies are becoming more prevalent. The solid to be examined is mounted so that the incident rays strike it in such a way that the photoejected electrons can easily pass through the ionization chamber slit into the analyser. A suitable probe is illustrated schematically in Fig. 2.4. The sample can be dissolved in a suitable solvent, and the solution dropped onto the probe face. Evaporation of the solvent leaves a suitable coating of the sample. Siegbahn *et al.*[12] have also made use of double-sided adhesive tape, one side being used to retain the sample, the other side making contact with the probe face. Frozen liquids and even solutions[36] have also been examined by X-ray photoelectron spectroscopy. A comparison of vapour phase and solid phase spectra of the same material has also been given by Siegbahn;[37] sharper but less intense spectra are obtained from the former. Appreciable shifts of peaks may also occur on passing from solid to gaseous samples of the same material (cf. water and ice, Chapter 3). We will mention this again in later sections.

ENERGY ANALYSIS OF THE EJECTED ELECTRONS, AND RELATED FACTORS AFFECTING THE RESOLUTION

Discussion of the way in which a spread of electron energies may be analysed must be concerned with resolution. This may be taken[34] as the width at half maximum height of one of the sharp peaks in the spectrum argon or xenon which correspond to the production of argon or xenon ions in their $^2P_{1/2}$ or $^2P_{3/2}$ states. Typically, the resolution in a commercial VUV spectrometer is 0·02 eV and in an X-ray one 1 eV. Electrons can be energy analysed in a number of ways, but modern instruments all employ focusing analysers (see below, and Chapter 3). One of the simplest methods, however, and the one to be first used in photoelectron spectroscopy, was by means of retarding grids.[14,39,40] In the early apparatus used by Turner,[40] a narrow pencil of photons was directed along the common axis of two cylindrical grids. Each grid was made from wire mesh spot-welded onto suitable cylindrical supports. These two grids were in turn surrounded by a cylindrical collector electrode, coaxial with the two wire-mesh grids, and the whole assembly enclosed in a glass envelope, which was evacuated. When vapour of a substance was admitted to the envelope, photoionization could occur along the common axis of the three electrodes. Electrons photoejected from the sample molecules passed through the wire-mesh grids to the collector (connected to a charge-sensitive amplifier) thereby registering an electron current.

To obtain an electron energy spectrum, an increasing retarding potential difference was applied between the wire-mesh grids, and the decreasing electron current plotted as a function of the retarding potential. As the retarding potential was increased, progressively more and more energetic electrons were prevented from reaching the collector. "Steps" in the current versus retarding potential curve thus showed the retarding potentials necessary to prevent electrons ejected from the different orbitals of the sample molecules from reaching the collector, and thus yielded the orbital ionization potentials.

The principal disadvantages of using straightforward cylindrical coaxial grid analysers are:

(i) poor resolution,
(ii) asymmetric peak shape,
(iii) high background from electrons scattered at the grids,
(iv) contamination of the grid surfaces by samples.

The main reason for the asymmetric peak shape is that electrons ejected in directions other than along the electron vector of the light beam are collected. Such electrons have a component of energy $E \cos^2 \theta$ in the direction of the retarding field, where θ represents the angle of divergence, and this results in all peaks in the spectrum having a low-energy tail. This effect can be reduced, and the resolution improved, by using slotted cylindrical grids (Fig. 2.5) so that electrons ejected along any line where θ is more than, say, 20° are prevented by discs from reaching the collector cylinder.

The use of retarding grids and a collector of spherical geometry offer a number of advantages in comparison with the cylindrical set-up.[40] There remain a number of drawbacks, however, and most photoelectron spectrometers in use today and certainly all the commercially available ones have focusing magnetic or electrostatic-type deflection analysers. These are capable of much higher resolution than the retarding field devices, but the much lower electron currents obtained necessitate the use of particle multipliers (see below). A high resolution focusing analyser of the magnetic

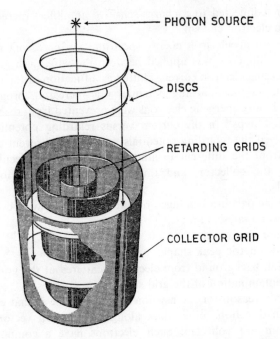

FIG. 2.5. Retarding field photoelectron spectrometer employing slatted coaxial cylindrical grids.

field type is described by Siegbahn *et al.*,[37] and one of lower resolution by May and Turner.[40] Electrostatic analysers are perhaps more convenient to use, however: they give a linear energy scale, whereas magnetic focusing analysers, since they discriminate by virtue of momentum, give a non-linear energy scale (since energy is proportional to the square of the momentum). A cylindrical-type sector analyser enabled the first very high-resolution photoelectron spectra to be obtained.[30] This analyser is illustrated schematically in Fig. 1.4, and can give a resolution of about 10 meV. The ejected electrons traverse an arc of $\pi/\sqrt{2}$ under the influence of the applied electrostatic field. The entrance slit of the analyser is positioned so that only electrons released along the electric vector of the photon beam (i.e. at 90° to the direction of photon propagation) or along paths not differing significantly from this are accepted by the analyser. Electrons with the appropriate kinetic energy to be focused pass through the analyser exit slit and impinge on the dynode system of an electron multiplier placed behind the slit. The exit slit width helps determine the peak width, narrower peaks generally being observed when the slit width is narrow. However, the bandwidth of low-energy electrons exceeds that of higher-energy electrons, so that the slit can be opened for the former without significant broadening taking place.

Other deflection-type analysers work on similar principles—one type which has been successfully incorporated into photoelectron spectrometers consists of two hemispherical plates.[41] Such an analyser has better focusing properties than the cylindrical plate analyser described above, and is therefore capable of higher resolution.[42,46] Other types of electron-energy analyser capable of high resolution are the parallel plate mirror type[38,47] and the cylindrical plate mirror type.[48,49] The latter has been the subject of an elegant theoretical treatment by Sar-El[50,51] and will doubtless be tried in photoelectron spectrometers as a comparison of the hemispherical plate and the cylindrical-mirror analysers[52] shows that the latter has several advantages. The theoretical resolving power depends upon instrumental design but the parameters common to all electrostatic analysers are the distance between the plates, the electron path and the voltage across the plates. Qualitatively, the manner in which these parameters affect the resolution can be intuitively grasped, but the exact comparison requires a rather more sophisticated mathematical approach. Plate surface potentials and contact potentials between different surfaces in these focusing types of analysers can degrade resolution and affect the energy scale, but their importance can be greatly diminished by a variety of treatments of the analyser plates including gold plating, gold evaporation, coating with soot or with colloidal graphite or by "electron velvetting".[60] It is often advantageous to accelerate ejected electrons out of the collision zone into the analysing region by suitable electrodes.[38] This results in an appreciable increase in the number of electrons reaching the detector, and therefore in an increase in sensitivity. It may lead to some distortion of the peaks, but from an analytical viewpoint this is a minor disadvantage offset by the gain in count rate. From the point of view of resolution it may also be advantageous to *retard* the electrons before entering the analyser. This is because it is easier to obtain narrow peaks with slow rather than fast electrons. Some instruments are supplied with a repeller or retarding electrode in the ionization chamber, and with such a device it is possible to obtain spectra by setting the sweep plates voltages to a constant optimum value, and obtaining an energy scan by varying the voltage on the repeller or retarding electrode.

The resolution is affected by reactions within the target chamber as well as by analyser design. For example, if all the molecules in the target chamber were moving about randomly with a velocity, u, and if electrons were ejected with a velocity, v, the maximum and minimum observed photoelectron energies will be given by:

$$E_{\max} = \tfrac{1}{2} m (v + u)^2, \tag{2.4}$$

$$E_{\min} = \tfrac{1}{2} m (v - u)^2. \tag{2.5}$$

Thus, the total broadening will be $2mvu$ and the half-width will be approximately mvu. The most probable velocity of molecules in the target chamber, $\bar{u}$, corresponds to the maximum of the Maxwellian distribution curve and is given by:

$$\bar{u} = \sqrt{\left(\frac{2KT}{M}\right)}, \tag{2.6}$$

$$\text{half-width} = mv \sqrt{\left(\frac{2KT}{M}\right)}. \tag{2.7}$$

The use of molecular beams in which all the sample molecules are moving in the same direction with the same velocity should be able to reduce this broadening to zero. However, the only photoelectron experiments to be carried out to date on molecular beams were not obtained under high-resolution conditions[35] so it is at present impossible to judge whether the use of molecular beams can in fact offer a significant improvement in resolution without corresponding improvements in analysers.

Another parameter which can contribute to the width of the

spectral peaks is the lifetime of the excited state produced. This is influenced by a number of factors:

(i) There may be a dissociation of the ion into fragments (i.e. excitation takes place to a repulsive part of a potential energy curve). Thus an appreciable variation in the lifetimes of different ions is to be expected. Lifetimes comparable to the period of one vibration (10^{-14} sec) may be encountered. Turner[29,30] has suggested that broadening arising out of fragmentation may be as much as 0·4 eV.

(ii) An ion decaying by a radiative deactivation or fluorescent process generally has a lifetime of about 10^{-8} sec for ultraviolet transitions which will therefore result in no significant broadening of UV photoelectron peak profiles. However, Turner points out that there could be an appreciable broadening due to such deactivation when X-rays are employed as the ionizing source, since the lifetime of the ion is inversely proportional to the cube of the energy.

(iii) Non-radiative transitions can occur to other ionic states, resulting in broadenings up to 0·1 eV.

ELECTRON MULTIPLIERS AND COUNTING EQUIPMENT

Electron multipliers are generally used for detecting the small electron fluxes emerging from the deflecting analysers used in electron spectrometry. These multipliers can vary from the "venetian-blind" type[53] enclosed in a glass tube about 9 cm long and 5 cm in diameter through to the more recently developed channel multipliers which can be as small as 0·2 mm in diameter and 10 mm in length. Gains up to 10^9 are possible with electron multipliers.

The channel multiplier consists essentially of a thin tube which has an internal coating of a high-resistance material.[54–56] A field of approximately 2000 V is applied by means of electrodes connected at each end. An electron entering the tube is accelerated until it strikes a wall. Secondary electrons are then emitted which are in turn accelerated and strike the wall, creating an "avalanche" of electrons. If the tube is straight, the gain is limited by ion feedback to about 10^5, but if it is curved, gains of up to 10^9 are possible. The gain of a particle multiplier may change quite markedly over a period of time. The older venetian-blind types are particularly prone to loss of gain because the dynode materials (often Cu–Be) are extremely sensitive to surface contaminants, which is a considerable nuisance in analytical work since some sample always gets through to the multiplier. The channel multipliers ("channeltrons") in current use, however, are more robust, and are also more suited to elevated temperature work so that it is possible to "bake out" impurities. All channeltrons seem to undergo a "clean-up" period when first operated, during which the gain decreases.[57,58] This change may be due to the desorption of gas from the inside of the device as a result of, for example, electron bombardment. Comparative quantitative measurements must therefore be postponed until after the clean-up period if they are to be reproducible. The possible "long-term fatigue" of channeltron multipliers after continuous electron bombardment at 10^{-6} torr has also been discussed by various authors.[58,59] Finally, it should be pointed out that electron multipliers are prone to serious loss of gain if, during use, the pressure around them rises to a level sufficient for sparking to occur, as might happen after a leak into the apparatus. As a safeguard the pressure should be frequently monitored, and the EHT supply cut off during any vacuum line manipulations such as altering the sample pressure, bleeding in calibrant, or during pump-out.

The counting equipment is standard: preamplifier, EHT, rate meter and recorder and/or punched tape output. The recorder drives the voltage sweep, although it may be advantageous to have this independent.

With X-ray spectra, the count rate is lower and more sophisticated equipment or a lot of counting time may be required to obtain a good spectrum.

REFERENCES

1. E. M. CLARKE, *Canad. J. Phys.*, 1954, **32**, 764.
2. C. E. KUYATT and J. A. SIMPSON, *Rev. Sci. Inst.*, 1967, **38**, 103.
3. R. S. BERRY, *Annual Review of Physical Chemistry*, 1969, **20**, 357.

4. A. E. GLASSGOLD, *Proceedings of the International Conference on Electronic and Atomic Collisions*, Lenningrad, 1967; Abstract Vol. p. 646.
5. A. D. BAKER, Ph.D. Thesis (London University), 1968, p. 166.
6. U. AMALDI, A. EGIDI, R. MARCOMERO and G. PIZZEITA, *Rev. Sci. Inst.*, 1969, **40**, 1001.
7. V. CERMAK, *J. Chem. Phys.*, 1966, **44**, 3781.
8. V. CERMAK, *Coll. Czech. Chem. Commun.*, 1968, **30**, 169.
9. V. CERMAK, *Coll. Czech. Chem. Commun.*, 1968, **33**, 2739.
10. V. CERMAK and Z. HERMAN, *Chem. Phys. Lett.*, 1968, **2**, 359.
11. V. CERMAK and A. NIEHAUS, *Phys. Rev. Lett.*, 1968, **21**, 1136.
12. K. SIEGBAHN *et al.*: ESCA—atomic, molecular and solid state structure studied by means of electron spectroscopy, *Nova Acta Regiae Societatis Scientarium Upsaliensis*, ser. IV, Vol. **20** (1967); revised edition in preparation.
13. D. W. TURNER, A. D. BAKER, C. BAKER and C. R. BRUNDLE, *High Resolution Molecular Photoelectron Spectroscopy*, Wiley & Sons Ltd., England, 1970.
14. F. I. VILESOV, B. L. KURBATOV and A. N. TERENIN, *Soviet Physics Doklady*, 1961, **6**, 490 (English edition).
15. J. A. R. SAMSON, *Techniques of Vacuum Ultraviolet Spectroscopy*, Wiley, New York, 1967.
16. W. R. S. GARTON, in: *Advances in Atomic and Molecular Physics*, Vol. 2 (1966), p. 93, Academic Press, 1966.
17. R. I. SCHOEN, *J. Chem. Phys.*, 1964, **40**, 1830.
18. P. H. DOOLITTLE and R. I. SCHOEN, *Phys. Rev. Lett.*, 1965, **14**, 348.
19. J. A. R. SAMSON, *Chem. Phys. Lett.* 1969, **4**, 257.
20. J. A. R. SAMSON and R. B. CAIRNS, *Phys. Rev.*, 1968, **173**, 80.
21. J. BERKOWITZ and W. A. CHIPKA, *J. Chem. Phys.*, 1969, **51**, 2341.
22. W. B. PEATMAN, T. B. BORNE and E. W. SCHLAG, *Chem. Phys. Lett.*, 1969, **3**, 492.
23. A. J. BLAKE and J. H. CARVER, *J. Chem. Phys.*, 1967, **47**, 1038.
24. F. J. COMES and H. J. SALZER, *Z. Naturf.*, 1964, **19a**, 1230.
25. J. S. SOLOMAN and W. L. BAUN, *Rev. Sci. Instr.* 1969, **40**, 1458.
26. P. MITCHELL and M. WILSON, *Chem. Phys. Lett.*, 1969, **3**, 389.
27. A. D. BAKER, C. R. BRUNDLE and D. W. TURNER, *Int. J. Mass Spect. Ion Phys.*, 1968, **1**, 443.
28. V. FUCHS and H. HOTOP, *Chem. Phys. Lett.* 1969, **2**, 71.
29. D. W. TURNER, *Nature*, 1967, **213**, 795.
30. D. W. TURNER, *Proc. Roy. Soc.*, A, 1968, **307**, 15.
31. A. MITCHELL and M. ZEMANSKY, *Resonance Radiation and Excited Atoms*, Cambridge U.P., 1961.
32. H. R. GRIEM, *Plasma Spectroscopy*, McGraw-Hill, 1964.
33. J. A. R. SAMSON, *Rev. Sci. Instr.*, 1969, **40**, 1174.
34. A. D. BAKER, *Accts. Chem. Res.*, 1970, **3**, 17.
35. M. J. WEISS, G. M. LAWRENCE and R. A. YOUNG, *J. Chem. Phys.*, 1970, **52**, 2867.
36. L. N. KRAMER and M. P. KLEIN, *J. Chem. Phys.*, 1969, **51**, 3620.
37. K. SIEGBAHN, C. NORDLING, G. JOHANSON, J. HEDMAN, P. F. HEDEN, K. HAMRIN, U. GELINS, A. T. BERGMARK, L. O. WERME, R. MANNE and Y.

BAER, *ESCA Applied to Free Molecules*, North Holland Publishing Co., Amsterdam, 1970.

38. J. H. D. ELAND and C. J. DANBY, *J. Sci. Instr.*, 1968, **1**, 1967.
39. G. ATELSON, K. HAMRIN, A. FAHLMAN, C. NORDLING and B. J. LINDBERG, *Spectrochim Acta*, 1967, **23A**, 2015.
40. D. W. TURNER and D. P. MAY, *J. Chem. Phys.*, 1966, **45**, 471.
41. Varian Associates, A.E.I. Ltd., and Vacuum Generators have all incorporated hemispherical analyses into their photoelectron spectrometers.
42. E. M. PURCELL, *Phys. Rev.*, 1938, **54**, 818.
43. C. E. KUYATT and J. A. SIMPSON, *Rev. Sci. Instr.*, 1967, **38**, 103.
44. E. N. LASSETTRE, A. SKERBELE, M. A. DILLON and K. J. ROSS, *J. Chem. Phys.*, 1968, **48**, 5066.
45. F. M. J. PICHANIK and J. A. SIMPSON, *Phys. Rev.*, 1968, **168**, 64.
46. A. SKERBELE, M. A. DILLON and E. N. LASSETTRE, *J. Chem. Phys.*, 1968, **49**, 5042.
47. G. A. HARROWES, *Rev. Sci. Instr.* 1955, **26**, 850.
48. V. ZASHKVARA, M. I. KORSANSKII and O. S. KOSMACHEV, *Soviet Physics—Technical Physics* (Eng. trans.), 1966, **11**, 96.
49. E. BLAUTH, *Z. Physik*, 1957, **147**, 278.
50. H. Z. SAR-EL, *Rev. Sci. Instr.*, 1967, **38**, 1210.
51. H. Z. SAR-EL, *Rev. Sci. Instr.*, 1968, **39**, 533.
52. H. HAFNER, J. A. SIMPSON and C. E. KUYATT, *Rev. Sci. Instr.*, 1968, **39**, 33.
53. J. S. ALLEN, *Rev. Sci. Instr.*, 1947, **18**, 739; venetian-blind multipliers are sold in the U.K. by E.M.I. Ltd.
54. L. HEROUX and H. E. HINTEREGGER, *Rev. Sci. Instr.*, 1960, **31**, 280.
55. G. W. GOODRICH and N. C. WILEY, *Rev. Sci. Instr.*, 1961, **32**, 846.
56. J. ADAMS and B. W. MARLEY, *Electronic Engineering*, 1965, **37**, 180.
57. R. REED, E. SHELLEY, J. BAKKE, T. SANDERS and J. McDANIEL, *IEEE Trans. Nucl. Sci.*, 1966, N.S., **16**, No. 1, 359.
58. W. G. WOLBER, B. D. KLETTE and H. K. LINTZ, *Rev. Sci. Instr.*, 1969, **40**, 1364.
59. A. EGIDI, R. MARCOMERO, G. PIZZELTA and F. SPERLI, *Rev. Sci. Instr.*, 1969, **40**, 88.
60. P. MARMET and L. KERWIN, *Canad. J. Phys.*, 1960, **38**, 787.

CHAPTER 3

FUNDAMENTAL FACTORS AFFECTING THE APPEARANCE OF A SPECTRUM

FACTORS INFLUENCING THE SHAPES OF BANDS IN THE SPECTRA

GENERAL POINTS

Broadly speaking, every band† in a photoelectron spectrum corresponds to an occupied atomic or molecule orbital of the sample substance. Naïvely, it might be supposed that doubly and triply degenerate orbitals would show up as bands with twice or thrice the intensity of non-degenerate orbitals. It might also be supposed that since every "band" of the spectrum represents essentially an orbital ionization potential, it would ideally have the form of just a single line at a particular energy value, whose width would be governed by the experimental limitations, such as natural line width, discussed in the previous chapter. This simple picture is in the main valid for X-ray excited spectra, but the most casual examination of any UV-excited spectra shows that for them it is manifestly of limited value. One of the main reasons for this is that the exciting X-ray natural line width is the dominant factor in causing broadening of bands in X-ray photoelectron spectra, whereas other factors are more important than natural width when UV-excitation is used. These other factors, which will be discussed

†At the outset of this discussion we must distinguish between *bands* and *peaks*. A band results from ionization from one orbital—it may be a single peak or it may have fine structure and thus consist of several peaks.

below, can cause bands to consist of a series of peaks, or to be split into multiplets.

Fine structure can occur because the energy imparted to an irradiated molecule is used to create both a free electron and an ion. The ion may be formed in vibrational, rotational and other excited states, e.g. different electronic states resulting from spin-orbit or Jahn–Teller effects. Any energy imparted to the ion must necessarily be reflected in the basic equation of photoelectron spectroscopy, which is an energy balance. Thus if the electron has been ionized from the nth orbital and the molecular ion is in the pth vibrationally excited state of energy $E_{vib(p)}$ and the qth rotationally excited state of $E_{rot(q)}$ the energy of the ejected electron is

$$E = h\nu - I_n - E_{vib(p)} - E_{rot(q)}. \tag{3.1}$$

Thus the photoelectron ionized from a given orbital may have one of several discrete energies depending on the degree of excitation of the molecular ion formed. In general, the more excited the ion the less will be the energy of the ejected electron. In principle for every value of E there will be a peak in the photoelectron spectra. It is always true that $I \gg E_{vib} > E_{rot}$ so that if the peaks due to different values of $E_{vib(p)}$ and $E_{rot(q)}$ show up at all it is as fine structure on the main ionization band. They may be unresolvable and thus simply broaden the ionization band. This will always be the case in X-ray excited spectra.

In principle, an ion formed by a photon-molecule collision could possess kinetic energy, and this would also detract from the value of the ejected photoelectron. However, the ion produced is so much more massive than the outgoing electron that it possesses, in comparison to the ejected electron, a negligible amount of kinetic energy (owing to the conservation of momentum) and thus this possibility is of no consequence in the interpretation of spectra. The factors which can influence the interpretation will now be considered in turn.

(a) Spin-orbit coupling

Removal of an electron from a completely filled p-orbital in an atom or molecule containing an even number of electrons, e.g.

5p in Xe, I_2, HI, CH_3I, H_2Te, etc., will give rise to an ion characterized by an orbital quantum number of 1, and possessing an unpaired
electron of spin $\pm \frac{1}{2}$. Consequently spin-orbit coupling can take
place to give two ionic states with $J = 3/2$ or $1/2$. These two states
have different energies, so that if other effects are negligible, the
band in the photoelectron spectrum due to this ionization should
be a doublet. Further, the intensities of the peaks would theoretically be expected to have a ratio of 2:1 (low-energy IP:higher IP)
corresponding to the statistical weighting of the states, but various
factors can cause deviations from this.

The energy separation between the two states can vary appreciably according to both the atom concerned and also the orbital
from which the electron is ejected. Thus removal of an electron from
a 3p orbital in argon can give rise to two ionic states, $^2P_{1/2}$ and $^2P_{3/2}$,
whose energies differ by 0·18 eV, whereas the corresponding ejections
of a 5p electron from a xenon atom can give rise to two $^2P_{1/2}$ and $^2P_{3/2}$
states which differ in energy by 1·3 eV. Ejection of electrons from
inner shells may lead to appreciably greater differences between the
components of a spin-orbit doublet. Similarly, spin-orbit states
$^2D_{5/2}$ and $^2D_{3/2}$ can result from fully occupied d-orbitals.

Spin-orbit coupling characteristic of an atom in a small molecule
is generally diminished as the atom becomes part of larger and
larger molecules, because the orbitals lose their pure s,p,d, etc.
nature even if they are formally "non-bonding". Thus the energy
difference between the $^2P_{1/2}$ and $^2P_{3/2}$ states of HCl^+ is 0·08 eV
whereas it is not observed experimentally in the ions resulting from
the ejection of a "chlorine 3p lone-pair electron" from methyl
chloride and other chloroalkanes.[1]

In practice, only iodine regularly shows spin-orbit split peaks in
many of its organic forms, the amount of splitting found in some
alkyl iodides being indicated in Fig. 3.1. Nevertheless, the effect
is still reasonably common for other atoms, e.g. O, S, Se, Br, transition metals.

(b) Vibrational fine structure

As has been stated above, the molecular ion which is produced
on ionization may be in vibrational and rotational excited states of

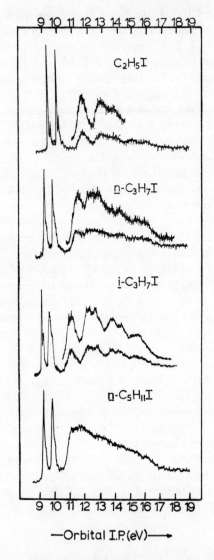

FIG. 3.1. The He-584-A excited spectra of some aliphatic iodoalkanes. The two sharp peaks in the region 8·5–10 eV correspond in every case to ionization from the iodine 5p orbital. There are two peaks present because removal of an electron from this orbital can give rise to ionic states differing in their total (spin/orbit) angular momentum (J).

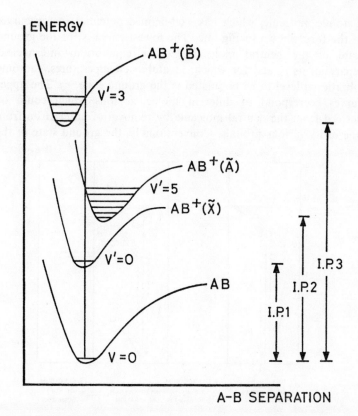

FIG. 3.2. Potential energy curves for the molecular ground state of a molecule, AB, and the three electronic states of the ion AB^+ resulting from the ejection of one electron from the three highest occupied orbitals of AB.

energies E_{vib} and E_{rot} respectively. E_{vib} and E_{rot} are smaller than I, but with a standard high-resolution VUV photoelectron spectrometer, vibrational fine structure can be observed easily. Rotational fine structure has also been detected with very high-resolution instruments. Analysis of the fine structure can give vibrational frequencies of the molecular ion and these can be related to the corresponding frequencies in the neutral molecule.

The origin of the fine structure is most easily seen in the case of a diatomic molecule, which has well-defined potential energy curves of the form shown in Fig. 3.2. The lowest curve is for the ground state of the neutral molecule, whose equilibrium internuclear separation is r_e and for which, at ambient temperatures, the only vibrational level to be populated is the ground state, v_0. The upper curves correspond to different molecular ions which could be derived from the neutral molecule by removal of an electron from one of its various orbitals. Conventionally, the ground state of the

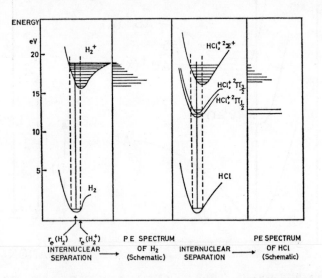

FIG. 3.3. The He-584-A photoelectron spectra of H_2 and HCl shown in schematic form alongside potential energy curve diagrams representing the processes occurring.

ion, i.e. the state formed by the ejections of an electron from the highest occupied orbital of the neutral molecule, is designated $(\tilde{X})$ and the higher states by $(\tilde{A})$ $(\tilde{B})$ $(\tilde{C})$, etc. (corresponding to IP_1, IP_2, IP_3 IP_4, etc., respectively). All these ions have vibrational energy levels characterized by v'_0, v'_1, v'_2, etc. The equilibrium internuclear distances in the ions may be greater, less or the same as that in the parent molecule depending whether the ejected electron came from a bonding, antibonding or non-bonding orbital. These factors will also determine how many vibrational excited states of the ion can be formed by ionizing acts. According to the Franck–Condon principle and the Born–Oppenheimer equation, the ionic vibrational state most likely to be formed is the lowest energy one, which, by virtue of its vibrational motion, can have an internuclear separation equal to that of the parent molecule. Thus, for the ions $(\tilde{X})$ $(\tilde{A})$ $(\tilde{B})$ of Fig. 3.2 this corresponds to $v' = 0$, $v' = 5$ and $v' = 3$, respectively. Other transitions are possible but less probable, and this is reflected in the photoelectron spectrum where the peak heights of vibrational series are proportional to the probabilities of transition. This is illustrated in Fig. 3.3, where the valence-shell spectra of H_2 and HCl are schematically shown alongside the potential energy-curve diagrams.

It follows that several ionization energies could be quoted, depending on how highly excited were the ions formed. In practice only two types of ionization energies are usually quoted:

(i) the *adiabatic ionization potential*, which is effectively the minimum possible energy which will free on electron from an orbital, and involves the simultaneous formation of an ion in its $v' = 0$ state, and,

(ii) the *vertical ionization potential*, which is the energy needed to free an electron from an orbital and simultaneously to form an ion in its vibronically "most probable" state, $v' \geqslant 0$.

Under the normal conditions for obtaining a spectrum the parent molecule is in the ground state, and the vertical IP is easily determined, being that associated with the major peak in the band. The adiabatic potential may be more difficult to assign, because the $v'_0 \leftarrow v_0$ transition may be so weak that it is not observed experimentally. Then it may possibly be deduced by extrapolation from the observable parts of vibrational series. If the ionization is from a non-bonding orbital the most probable transition is the $v'_0 \leftarrow v_0$ and the vertical and adiabatic IPs coincide. In a well-defined vibrational series the separation between peaks can be readily related to a vibrational frequency of the ion.

This frequency in turn may be related to the corresponding frequency in a parent molecule and from the shift in frequency it may

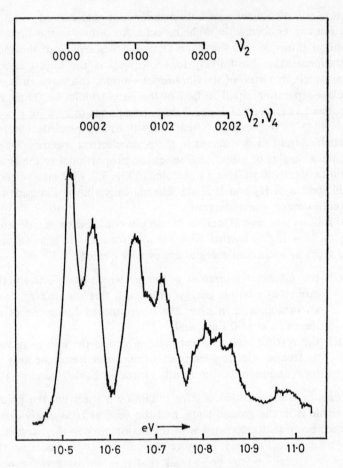

Fig. 3.4. The first (π) band in the photoelectron spectrum of ethylene, showing the presence of vibrational series in v_2 and v_4.

be deduced whether the electron has been ionized from a bonding or antibonding orbital (see below for N_2, H_2O).

These arguments may be extended to more complex molecules, although one is then dealing with n-dimensional potential energy surfaces rather than two-dimensional curves, and more than one vibrational mode may be excited by ionization from a particular orbital (see H_2O below). In favourable cases different vibrational series within one band may be distinguished in the fine structure of a photoelectron spectrum (e.g. the π-band in the spectrum of ethylene Fig. 3.4).[1,2] Typically the peaks of one series are less intense, and, of course, the spacings are different. The changes in vibrational frequencies on going from a molecular to an ionic state may be so large that it is difficult to relate an ionic mode of vibration with one of the molecular modes. Despite these difficulties, analysis of the vibrational fine structure has proved extremely useful in interpreting the photoelectron spectra of complex molecules.

(c) *Dissociation*

In some cases there may be a high probability of producing an ion in a level above the dissociation continuum. If the ion can also be produced in stable vibrational levels, the spacings of these levels, and hence of the peaks in a photoelectron band, will converge rapidly as the continum is neared. The spectrum for H_2 (Fig. 3.3) illustrates this type of situation. If *all* ionizing acts result in dissociation, the photoelectron band will have the appearance of a hump containing no fine structure.

Predissociation can also occur by potential energy curve crossing between the stable ionic state and a repulsive state. Such a crossing over is distinguished in a spectral band containing fine structure by an abrupt termination of the sharp fine structure, and usually corresponds to a known appearance potential of a fragment ion. The spectra of SF_6 and HCN provide examples of this phenomenon (Fig. 3.5).[1]

(d) *The Jahn–Teller effect*

All electric-dipole allowed excitations from one of a set of degenerate orbitals in a non-linear molecule give rise to two or more excited states of different symmetries than the parent molecule instead of multiply degenerate states of the same symmetry. This is the Jahn–Teller effect, and is of course applicable to the photoelectron spectrometry of molecules containing degenerate orbitals.

The origin and full consequences of the effect are complex. There

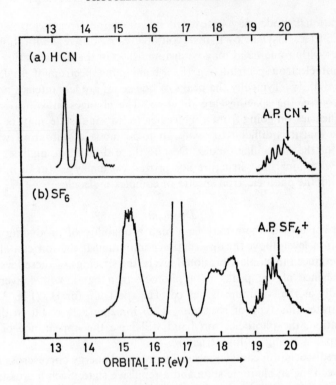

FIG. 3.5. The He-584-A photoelectron spectra of HCN and SF$_6$.

are both *static* and *dynamic* effects. The former can be visualized simply, in a manner analogous to the treatment of the effect in elementary texts on ligand field theory; if it is assumed that electrons in the degenerate levels are localized in equivalent bonds, removal of one electron will lead to the lengthening of one of the bonds and hence to a change in molecular symmetry and loss of degeneracy. The dynamic effect is connected with changes in angular momentum which take place on ionization and the simple analogy is the effect on a centrifuge containing two balanced tubes (equivalent to degenerate levels) when one of the tubes is removed. At present, the interrelationship of these effects and their exact nature is not fully understood. Their practical consequences is that in the photoelectron spectrum one observes a band with more than one maximum (corresponding to the ionic states of different symmetries) rather than a smooth band with one maximum. The first example of the effect to be found in photoelectron spectrometry was for methane, where ionization from one of the triply degenerate $2pt_2$ orbitals (see in succeeding pages) produces the above effect (Fig. 3.6).[1,2]

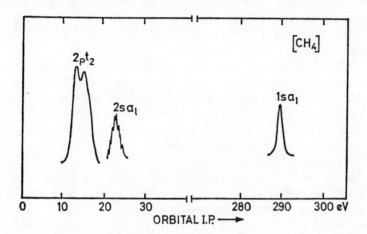

Fig. 3.6. Bands in the photoelectron spectrum of methane. This is a composite spectrum, made up from the 304-A excited spectrum (two bands on the left) and the Al-K_α X-ray excited spectrum (band on right).

(e) *Exchange splitting and multiplet splitting*

These forms of band splitting arise when electron ejection from a ground state molecule containing an unpaired electron gives an ion with two unpaired electrons. They are not very common and are dealt with in detail in the review by Brundle and Robin.[3]

FACTORS INFLUENCING THE POSITION OF BANDS IN THE SPECTRA

It is a basic tenet of photoelectron spectroscopy that the bands in the spectrum correspond to the molecular orbitals of the target molecule. Thus, the ionization potentials can be thought of as the negative of the molecular orbital energies or eigenvalues. This assumption, which is in essence Koopmans' theorem,[4] has formed the basis of all the rigorous analyses of photoelectron spectra. The theorem has limitations,[5] but, in the main, it has proved both convenient and adequate provided the possible deviations are borne in mind. In extreme cases, these deviations can, for example, result in the ordering of orbital ionization potentials being different from the ordering of orbital eigenvalues. The correlation between molecular orbital theory and spectra is brought out in the examples discussed below.

Before turning to the examples, we must emphasize that molecular ionization potentials should be compared only with the orbital and eigenvalue solutions of SCF equations, and not with the equivalent (e.g. hybrid) orbitals and energies obtained from them by a unitary transformation. This is an extremely important distinction to make, because although SCF-orbital and hybrid orbital treatments can be regarded as equivalent approaches for describing the ground-state chemistry of a molecule, only the former are useful for discussing individual orbital energies, orbital compositions and for calculating any type of spectroscopic transition energies. Hybrid, or "localized", orbitals are of value to the chemist who wishes to deduce the likelihood of bond formation and the shapes of molecules, but these orbitals do not diagonalize the matrix of SCF operators, and hence are unsuitable for discussing excited states. The hybrid orbitals may be derived from the overall wavefunction of a ground-state molecule by a unitary transformation, which alters neither the total energy nor the total electron density thus enabling a set of hybrid orbitals to be acceptable for describing ground-state properties. The unitary transformation, however, does of course affect the individual molecular orbital compositions and this is why only the SCF-orbitals are acceptable for discussions of individual orbitals, and for describing processes resulting from electronic transitions from individual orbitals. The distinctions between the localized (hybrid) and delocalized (SCF) molecular orbital approaches are discussed in detail elsewhere.[6–8] Urch sums it up: "The two models are quite complementary, depending more on the questions being asked about the molecule, rather than on the molecule itself."[3,8]

The forms of the SCF MOs can be deduced by considering which orbitals of the constituent atoms are available for forming molecular orbitals, and combining together those of appropriate energies and symmetries. The electronic configuration can then be derived by filling these orbitals with the appropriate number of electrons according to the Aufbau principle. The relative energies of the resultant MOs will, of course, be uncertain, but these can be inferred either intuitively, or from the photoelectron spectrum in a number of cases, and then compared with SCF calculations.

These points can be illustrated by reference to the methane molecule. The combining atomic orbitals we need to consider are C 1s, C 2s, C 2p and H 1s. The C 1s orbital is too different in energy from the other atomic orbitals to enter into any MO formation, thus the deepest orbital of the methane molecule will be predominantly C 1s ($1sa_1$). This corresponds to the band in the photoelectron spectrum at *ca.* 290 eV (Fig. 3.6). The C 2s and H 1s orbitals can combine to form one orbital of type ψ C 2s ψ H 1s, whilst the C 2p and H 1s orbitals can combine to form three orbitals of type ψ C 2p ψ H 1s. There are ten electrons to accommodate in the methane molecule; two are accounted for in the $1sa_1$ orbital, therefore the one ψ C 2s ψ H 1s ($2sa_1$) and the three ψ C 2p ψ H 1s ($2pt_2$) orbitals must be fully occupied. These give rise to the bands at *ca.* 23 eV and *ca.* 13 eV in the photoelectron spectra. The band at 13 eV is Jahn–Teller split, because it represents ionization from one of a set of three degenerate orbitals (see above). The band should in theory have the appearance of a triplet, but in this case it is not resolved. A clear triplet is, however, plainly seen in the corresponding band in the spectrum of SiH_4.

EXAMPLES OF THE PHOTOELECTRON SPECTRA OF SIMPLE ATOMS AND MOLECULES

The spectra of a few atoms and small molecules will now be discussed to illustrate the principles discussed above.

(a) *Rare gases*

The main features of the spectra, shown for He, Ne and Ar in Fig. 3.7 in a stylized fashion, are peaks which correspond to the different atomic orbitals. The complicating effects of spin-orbit coupling, of X-ray satellite bands and of Auger peaks, have been

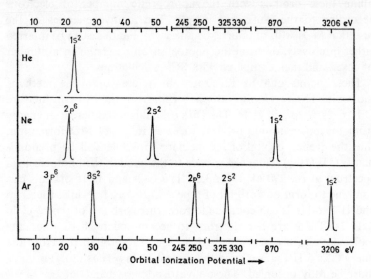

Fig. 3.7. Schematic diagram representing bands due to ionization from the different atomic orbitals in the X-ray photoelectron spectra of the rare gases.[13]

taken out of the figure for simplicity. The spin-orbit components of the neon 2p and argon 3p peaks are in fact unresolved in the X-ray excited spectra, but the argon $^2P_{1/2}$ and $^2P_{3/2}$ peaks are resolved at 250·6 and 248·5 eV, respectively. The spin-orbit components of the outermost "p" level peaks in the rare gas spectra are resolved only when UV-excitation is used. The sharp peaks present in the rare gas X-ray and UV-excited spectra enable the energy scan of the spectrometer used to be calibrated, since some of the ionization potentials of these gases are very accurately known from other sources.

(b) *Nitrogen*

Nitrogen is a simple homonuclear diatomic molecule whose molecular orbital energy diagram is given in a number of standard texts on valency and general chemistry.[9-12] The molecular orbitals as a first-row homonuclear diatomic molecule are formed from the 1s, 2s, $2p_x$, $2p_y$, and $2p_z$ orbitals of the constituent atoms. The σ-bonding (σ_g) and σ-antibonding orbitals (σ_u) which can be formed

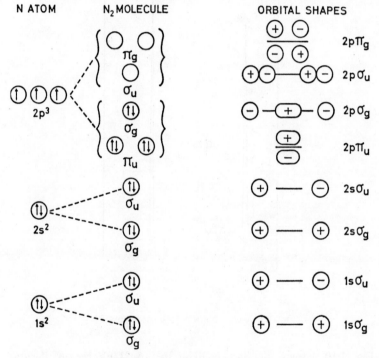

FIG. 3.8. Molecular orbital energy diagram for nitrogen. Energy levels and separations are not to scale.

are, in increasing energy, $1s\sigma_g$, $1s\sigma_u$, $2s\sigma_g$, $2s\sigma_u$, $2p_x\sigma_g$ and $2p_x\sigma_u$. The $2p_y$ atomic orbitals can combine to produce π-bonding ($2p_y\pi_u$) and π-antibonding ($2p_y\pi_g$) orbitals, as can the $2p_z$AOs, to form

$(2p_z\pi_u)$ and $(2p_z\pi_g)$ molecular orbitals. The two π_u orbitals are degenerate, and so are the two π_g orbitals. The various combinations and resultant energy levels are shown in Fig. 3.8 and Fig. 3.9 shows the X-ray excited spectrum. The UV-excited spectrum, given in

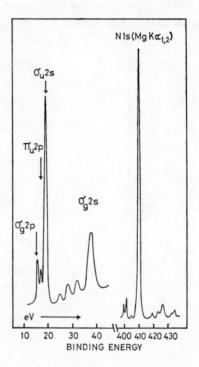

FIG. 3.9. X-ray photoelectron spectrum of N_2 [13]

Fig. 3.10, shows the fine detail of the 15–21 eV region. Because there are fourteen electrons to accommodate in a N_2 molecule, only seven of the above molecular orbitals are occupied. Two of these orbitals are degenerate, thus we would expect to see six peaks in the total photoelectron spectrum. Examination of the X-ray excited spectrum shows five major peaks, and a number of minor peaks

arising from either X-ray satellites or Auger emission. The single
peak at highest binding energy, in the region expected for N 1s
core electrons, indicates that the $1s\sigma_g$ and $1s\sigma_u$ orbital ionization
potentials are too close for different $1s\sigma_g$ and $1s\sigma_u$ photoelectron
peaks to be resolved. The differences in energies between the molecular orbitals formed from the 1s, 2s, and 2p atomic orbitals are clearly
shown in the spectrum. Thus the gross features of the spectrum are
in agreement with the basic deductions of simple MO theory.

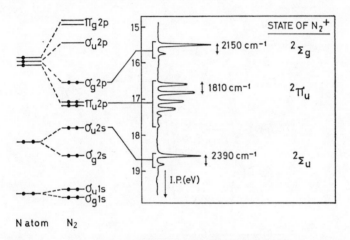

FIG. 3.10. UV photoelectron spectrum of N_2.

The 584-A excited spectrum has only three bands corresponding
to ionization from the $2s\sigma_u$, $2\pi_u$, and $2p\sigma_g$ orbitals. The main difference between this spectrum and the X-ray excited spectrum over the
same region is that there is much better resolution, e.g. fine structure,
which is a major feature of the band centred at 17 eV, and a minor
feature of the other two bands. The spacing of the peaks in the three
bands gives the vibrational frequencies in the $(\tilde{X})$, $(\tilde{A})$, $(\tilde{B})$ states of
N_2^+ to be 2150, 1810 and 2390 cm^{-1} respectively (1 eV = 8065·7
cm^{-1}). These frequencies may be compared with that of 2345 cm^{-1}

in the N_2 molecule. These changes in frequency would normally indicate (see preceding pages) that the top three occupied orbitals were, in order of increasing ionization potential, very weakly bonding, moderately strongly bonding, and very weakly antibonding. Care must, however, be exercised in interpreting these observations. For example, one might erroneously infer from the above results that it would be quite easy to split up a N_2 molecule into constituent atoms, since the atoms are held together almost exclusively

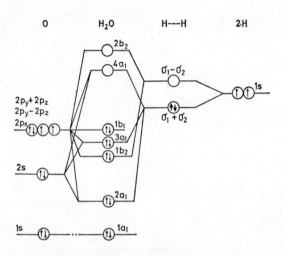

FIG. 3.11. Molecular orbital energy diagram for water.

by π-bonding; the σ-overlaps being ineffective. However, the bonding strengths deduced from the photoelectron spectrum apply only to the ground state molecule at its equilibrium internuclear separation. When electronic charge is removed from the N_2 π-orbitals, the N atoms move apart, and it is only at an increased N—N spacing that the σ-bonding becomes effective. It is in fact because the maximum bonding overlaps of σ- and π-orbitals are at different internuclear separations that the dissociation energy of a $N\equiv N$ triple bond is much greater than, and not equal to three times the value for a N—N bond.

(c) *Water*

The appropriate combinations of atomic orbitals to give the most important molecular orbitals of water are shown in Fig. 3.11. The oxygen 1s orbital is of too low an energy and of too small a radius to be involved in molecular bonding to any extent. The deepest

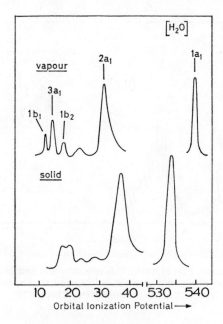

FIG. 3.12. X-ray PE spectrum of water.[13]

filled orbital in water is therefore basically pure O 1s, containing two electrons. There are eight other electrons to be accounted for, and as none of the proposed orbitals are degenerate, there should be four other bands in the complete photoelectron spectrum, making a grand total of five. The "O 1s" and the "O 2s/H 1s-bonding" bands would not be expected to be observed in the UV-excited spectrum. Both the X-ray[13] and UV-excited[14] spectra are shown in Figs. 3.12 and 3.13 and again fine structure is clearly shown in the UV-excited spectrum. There is a marked difference in the detail of the X-ray PE spectra obtained on samples in the solid and vapour phases.

There is a blurring of the solid-state spectrum possibly because of hydrogen bonding and a big shift in actual values of the IP, which

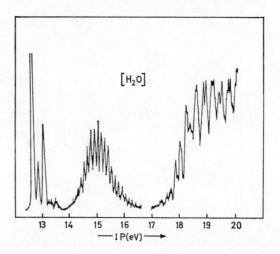

FIG. 3.13. UV-PE spectrum of water. This spectrum was obtained by setting the analyser deflection plates to a constant voltage and then sweeping through a range of repelling voltages (see Chapter 2).

is believed to be connected with the Fermi level of the solid. Nevertheless, there is general agreement between MO theory and the spectra. Table 3.1, which gives the IPs and eigenvalues, calculated by various workers[15–19] illustrates how quantitative this agreement is. Analysis of the fine structure supports the MO interpretation. The first band (vertical and adiabatic IP = 12·61 eV) by its sharpness indicates ionization from a weakly bonding orbital. The irregularity of the peak intensities suggests that at least two vibrational series are present. Two series can be assigned with vibrational frequencies of 3200 ∓ 50 and 1380 ∓ 50 cm^{-1} which compare with the symmetric stretching ν_1, and the bending ν_2, modes of water, 3652 and

TABLE 3.1. OBSERVED IONIZATION POTENTIALS AND CALCULATED
EIGENVALUES FOR THE WATER MOLECULE
(in eV)

IPs	1st $(1b_2)$	2nd $(3a_1)$	3rd $(1b_1)$	Refs.
Experimental	12·61	13·7	17·22	14
Calculated	11·79	13·2	18·55	15
	13·14	14·50	17·50	16
	10·95[a]	12·68[a]	16·98[a]	17
	14·18[b]	16·19[b]	19·82[b]	17
	13·79	15·84	19·56	18
	10·94	12·92	17·22	19

[a]Seven basic functions.
[b]Twenty-six basic functions.

1595 cm^{-1}. This suggests a basically non-bonding orbital, i.e. the oxygen "lone pair".†

The second band (vertical IP 14·7 eV adiabatic IP 13·7 eV) has pronounced fine structure. The spacings between the peaks are regular (0·120 eV) and correspond to a vibrational frequency of 975 ∓ 50 cm^{-1}. This must be associated with the bending mode and indicates a strongly bonding orbital. As shown in Fig. 3.14 this orbital contains a high proportion of H—H bonding. Removal of an electron from it would therefore be expected to modify the H—H separation, i.e. cause the molecule to bend.

†Photoelectron spectroscopy shows that the lone pairs of electrons do not exist as independent non-bonding electrons. Nevertheless, to avoid continual qualification the terms "lone pair" or "non-bonding" electrons will be used in the usual way.

The third band (vertical IP 18·55 eV, adiabatic IP 17·22 eV) has fine structure but it is not so well resolved. There are clearly two vibrational series, in that each peak has the appearance of a doublet and close analysis assigns values of 2990 $\mp$ 100 and 1610 $\mp$ 100 cm^{-1} to these. The first of these frequencies is much lower than that of ν_1 in the molecular ground state suggesting an orbital associated with strong O—H bonding, i.e. $\psi 1b_2$ orbital in Fig. 3.14. Ionization from this orbital would also be expected to excite the bending mode and it is seen to do so. The orbital has H—H antibonding character so that removal of an electron from it would be expected to reduce the H—O—H bond angle and increase the vibrational frequency of the bending mode. This increase would be opposed by the increase in the O—H separation resulting from removal of an electron from an O—H bonding orbital. Since the frequency of the bending mode is almost the same in molecule and ion, it is inferred that these opposing effects are almost equal. Again it is clear that care is necessary when applying the generalizations discussed above to detailed spectra.

The appearance potential of OH$^+$ ions is known by other methods to be 18·2 eV and since the formation of OH$^+$ must involve the removal of an electron from the H—O—H bonding orbital, the spectrum might be expected to show evidence of dissociation or predissociation phenonoma. The loss of fine structure coincident with the appearance potential suggests that the molecule is undergoing decomposition by a predissociation process.

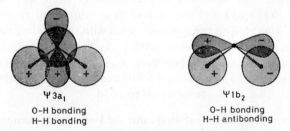

$\Psi 3a_1$

O–H bonding
H–H bonding

$\Psi 1b_2$

O–H bonding
H–H antibonding

FIG. 3.14. Combination of hydrogen 1s and oxygen 2p orbitals to give bonding orbitals of water.

COMPLICATING FACTORS

Sometimes additional peaks or bands of unexpected intensity are to be observed in a spectrum. The principle causes of these complicating factors will be dealt with briefly.

AUGER EFFECT AND AUTOIONIZATION

If an electron is ejected from the K-shell of an atom it is possible for the vacancy to be filled by an electron from the L-shell. The L to K transition may either be accompanied by radiation (*fluorescence*) or it may be radiationless, in which case the excess energy may be used to eject an electron from one of the higher shells, e.g. M-shell. This latter process is known as the *Auger effect* and is the preferred by the lighter elements to fluorescence. Auger peaks are commonly observed in X-ray PE spectra. As they result from a secondary process which is independent of the energy of the incident photon, provided that it is great enough to eject an electron from the K-shell, they may be detected by varying the source energy. The application of Auger spectroscopy is dealt with later, but it should be noted that Auger peaks do occur in X-ray PE spectra.

Autoionization is similar to, and one authority[20] describes it as identical with, the Auger effect. In the Auger effect, however, an inner electron is ejected completely, whereas in autoionization it is merely promoted into an orbital of higher energy. Thus, the Auger effect can always take place provided that the incident energy is greater than the binding energy of the inner electron, but autoionization can *only* occur if the impacting photon quantum hv is equal to the difference in energy between the ground state and some excited state of the neutral molecule, in which a normally inner electron occupies an outer orbital. Price[21] describes autoionization as "a process in which the excited inner electron gives up its energy to a more loosely bound electron, thereby ejecting it by a kind of internal electron bombardment". This latter definition implies a process different from Auger. The first step is the excitation of the molecule by absorption of a photon. The second stage is an electron falling into the positive hole created during excitation, thereby releasing sufficient energy to eject an electron. The end product is thus a singly charged ion, whereas in the Auger process it is a doubly charged ion. Autoionization will only occur if the incident photon energy is just sufficient to effect the primary excitation, whereas the Auger effect can occur whenever the incident energy is equal or greater than that required to eject an inner electron.

One consequence is that if the energy of the incident photons is close to that which results in autoionization, bands may be much more intense and have more fine structure than if they had been due simply to direct photoionization. Thus oxygen bands in the 13-eV and 16·5-eV region are much more pronounced in the spectrum obtained with neon (16·9 eV) photons than with helium (21·2 eV) photons because oxygen has an excited molecular state about 17 eV above the ground state.[21] The spectra of hydrogen and deuterium, which do not have available autoionizing levels at 17 eV, do not show this effect. Autoionization has been held responsible for the appearance of "spurious" peaks in the photoelectron spectrum of water excited at some wavelengths[23] and has been shown to account for features of spectroscopic interest in a number of spectra of simple molecules.

Another related, but rare, process is when some of the incident photon energy is used simultaneously to excite a molecule and to eject an electron from it. The energy of the ejected electron will be less than expected by the amount required to excite the molecule.

Satellite lines in the source account for some extra, weak, bands in X-ray PE spectra. These result from atomic readjustments after double ionization. If an electron is removed from the L-shell as well as the K-shell then a subsequent transfer of an electron from the L- to the K-shell will be accompanied by radiation of higher wave number than would result from a L to K transition in a singly ionized ion.[20] Thus the source has satellite lines which give rise to the satellite peaks which are to be seen in many of the spectra in Siegbahn's book.[13]

It is desirable for some purposes to use different sources, for example, a high-energy source may be necessary to eject tightly bound electrons, or a source of energy close to the peak of interest may be desirable to study the fine structure in detail (when $hv \approx I$, E_{elec} is small and the resolution is good). However, the relative intensity of the peaks may change because ionization cross-sectional areas are dependent upon the energy of the incident photons. The variations in cross-sectional area are fairly well understood for inner shell electrons (see Chapter 6) but the converse is true for valence shell electrons, where various factors such as *intensity stealing* i.e. one band "stealing" some of nearby band, complicates things.

Finally there exist the possibilities of secondary reactions in the target chamber or sample decomposition on the way to the target chamber. Examples of both are given in Chapter 6. The effects may be to vary peak intensities, to introduce "spurious" peaks (decomposition products) or even to give a "spurious" spectrum in which the spectrum of the sample is negligible compared with products of reactions undergone by the sample on the way to the target chamber.

REFERENCES

1. D. W. TURNER, C. BAKER, A. D. BAKER and C. R. BRUNDLE, *Molecular Photoelectron Spectroscopy*, Wiley, London, 1970.
2. A. D. BAKER, C. BAKER, C. R. BRUNDLE and D. W. TURNER, *Int. J. Mass Spec. Ion Phys.*, 1968, **1**, 285.
3. C. R. BRUNDLE and M. ROBIN in *Determination of Organic Structures by Physical Methods*, Vol. III (eds. F. NACHOD and G. ZUCKERMAN), Academic Press, New York, 1971.
4. T. KOOPMANS, *Physica*, 1934, **1**, 104.
5. W. G. RICHARDS, *Int. J. Mass Spec. Ion Phys.*, 1969, **2**, 419.
6. D. J. ROYER, *Bonding Theory*, McGraw-Hill, New York, 1968.
7. C. A. COULSON, *Valence*, 2nd ed., Oxford University Press, Oxford, 1961.
8. D. S. URCH, *Orbitals and Symmetry*, Penguin, Harmondsworth, 1970.
9. J. N. MURRELL, S. F. A. KETTLE and J. M. TEDDER, *Valence Theory*, 2nd ed., Wiley, London, 1970.
10. H. B. GRAY, *Electrons and Chemical Bonding*, Benjamin, New York, 1965.
11. E. CARTMELL and G. W. A. FOWLES, *Valence and Molecular Structure*, 3rd ed., Butterworths, London, 1966.
12. R. MAHAN, *University Chemistry*, 2nd ed., Addison Wesley.
13. K. SIEGBAHN *et al.*, *ESCA of Free Atoms and Molecules*, North-Holland, Amsterdam, 1970.
14. C. R. BRUNDLE and D. W. TURNER, *Proc. Roy. Soc.* A, 1968, **307**, 27.
15. F. O. ELLISON and H. SCHULL, *J. Chem. Phys.*, 1955, **23**, 2348.
16. J. W. MOSKOWITZ and M. C. HARRISON, *J. Chem. Phys.*, 1955, **43**, 3550.
17. S. ALUNG, R. M. PITZER and S. I. CHAN, *J. Chem. Phys.*, 1968, **49**, 2071.

18. D. NEUMANN and J. W. MOSKOWITZ, *J. Chem. Phys.*, 1968, **49**, 2056.
19. E. SWITKES, R. M. STEVENS and W. N. LIPSCOMB, *J. Chem. Phys.*, 1969, **51**, 5229.
20. H. G. KUHN, *Atomic Spectra*, Longmans, London, 1962.
21. W. C. PRICE, *Molecular Spectroscopy*, Inst. Petroleum, 1968.
22. A. D. BAKER, C. R. BRUNDLE and D. W. TURNER, *Int. J. Mass Spec. Ion Phys.*, 1968, **1**, 443.

CHAPTER 4

INTERPRETATION OF UV-PHOTOELECTRON SPECTRA

GENERAL COMMENTS

Even if it were technically possible it would not always be practicable or desirable to subject every compound examined by photoelectron spectroscopy to a full molecular orbital treatment. It is nevertheless essential to be able to ascribe spectral features with molecular characteristics in the way that organic chemists treat infrared and NMR spectra. This chapter shows how such an approach is possible with UV-excited photoelectron spectra, the next performs the same task for X-ray excited photoelectron spectra. Such an approach must be based on the correlation of features of the spectra of a large number of well-known compounds.

The technique is not yet sufficiently advanced to permit a full interpretation of the photoelectron spectra of every substance. It is, however, possible to make generalizations about some spectral features, particularly about shifts in peak positions for a series of related compounds and about bands which are due to ionization from both lone-pair and π-orbitals.

The attempts at interpretation have consisted largely of assigning bands in the spectra to molecular orbitals in the sample molecule and then trying to explain the differences in IP for the same, or corresponding, molecular orbital in related compounds. It is commonly assumed that:

(i) Changes in the energies of molecular orbitals can be

55

correlated specifically with changes in the substitution pattern of the molecule.

(ii) Molecular orbitals can often be treated as being localized on an atom (e.g. a lone-pair orbital) or between a relatively small number of atoms, e.g. a π-orbital.

Two principle effects of changes in substitution pattern may be noted in the spectra. Firstly, the substituent may change the polarity of or charge distribution within the molecule, as a result of inductive effects or changes in electronegativity. Thus the electrons in the orbital under examination may be more firmly held and hence have a higher IP or the converse may be true. Secondly, the substituent may have an orbital of such energy and symmetry that it can interact with the orbital under consideration, i.e. exert a mesomeric effect. These factors will be considered in more detail below.

ELECTRONEGATIVITY AND INDUCTIVE EFFECTS

Electronegativity is a measure of the attraction that an atom *within a molecule* has for electrons. There are two useful ways in which the concept can be applied in the interpretation of spectra. Firstly, one can compare a series in which one atom or group is replaced by others of different electronegativity. The replacement of an atom by another of higher electronegativity will result in the increase of the ionization potentials of orbitals associated with adjacent atoms; the electrons being more firmly held by the more electronegative atom. When the replacement atom is of lower electronegativity the converse is true. Other orbitals will be either similarly affected or unaffected depending on the position of the replacement atom or group within the molecule and its electronegativity. Electronegativity correlations may be used to predict the orbital ionization potentials associated with atoms X, Y, Z, etc., in a series of molecules W–X, W–Y, W–Z, etc. For example, in the series R-hal, where R is constant the ionization potentials of the halogen lone pair are proportional to the electronegativities of the halogen atoms (Fig. 4.1).[1] So far electronegativity correlations

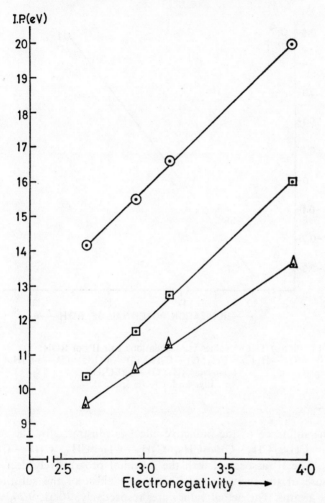

Fig. 4.1. Plot of Pauling electronegativities vs. IPs of halogen lone pair orbitals for H-Hal (□) and Me or Ph-Hal (△) and orbital IPs for H-Hal (○).

have been made with the Pauling or Pauling-type values, but it is possible that with better understanding of spectra the orbital electronegativities of Hinze and Jaffe also may be of value.[2-5]

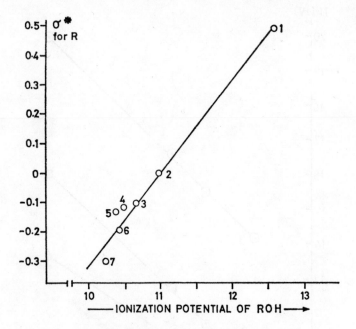

FIG. 4.2. Plot of Taft σ^* values vs. oxygen lone pair IPs of ROH:
R = (1) —H; (2) —CH$_3$; (3) —C$_2$H$_5$; (4) —n-C$_3$H$_7$; (5) —n-C$_4$H$_9$;
(6) —iso-C$_3$H$_7$; (7) —tert-C$_4$H$_9$
(see Fig. 4.6 for ROH spectra).

The influence of the inductive effect is illustrated by the series CH$_2$=CH$_2$, CH$_3$—CH=CH$_2$, C$_2$H$_5$—CH=CH$_2$, C$_3$H$_7$—CH= CH$_2$. The IP associated with the π-orbital progressively decreases because of the increasing $+I$, inductive effect of the substituent alkyl groups. The actual values are, respectively, 10·51, 9·74, 9·61, 9·51 eV.[6]

Another measure of electron withdrawing or donating capacity is provided by Hammett or Taft coefficients σ, σ^+, or σ^*.[7] These are well known in organic chemistry and many values for particular groups have been determined, mainly from kinetic experiments. Figure 4.2 shows that for alcohols there is a correlation between Taft

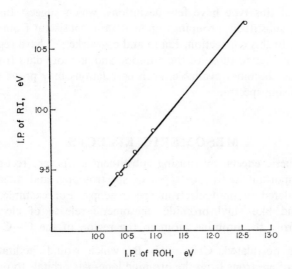

FIG. 4.3. Plot of iodine 5p lone pair IPs of alkyl iodides against the oxygen 2p lone pair IPs of the corresponding alcohols:

R = (1) —H; (2) —CH$_3$; (3) —C$_2$H$_5$; (4) n-C$_3$H$_7$; (5) —i-C$_3$H$_7$; (6) —n-C$_5$H$_{11}$.

σ^* values for the alkyl substituents, and the IPs corresponding to the oxygen "lone-pair" orbitals, which might be expected to experience changes in charge density with charge in substituent group.[8] A similar correlation has been found for σ^* and iodine lone-pair IPs in alkyl iodides. These correlations are interesting, but by no means perfect. Differences may arise because the σ^* values are not a true representation of all the factors which can affect orbital ionization potentials, and furthermore, σ^* values are obtained on solutions whereas UV-photoelectron spectra are obtained on samples in the vapour phase, and it is possible that with the change of phase there are changes in steric configurations with consequent changes in polarizing effects. A more straightforward type of correlation is obtained when the lone-pair ionization potentials of two related series, e.g. ROH and RI, are plotted against another (Fig. 4.3).

Graphs of this type have few deviations, which suggest that the effects of substituent groupings upon IPs are consistent from series to series. In this connection, Eland and co-workers[9] have reported similar findings to those of the authors, and as more data from related series becomes available, such correlations may prove useful in diagnosing spectra.

MESOMERIC EFFECTS

Mesomeric effects, by causing substituent shifts, are recognized to be important in various types of spectroscopy, and must also be considered in photoelectron spectroscopy. For example, in a compound like vinyl bromide, mesomeric release of electronic charge from the bromine atom to the region of the C—C bond could be postulated, $CH_2 = CH—Br$, which would facilitate the removal of electrons from the bromine lone-pair orbitals to orbitals associated with the C—C bond. This would tend to make the π-IP of $CH_2 = CHBr$ lower than that of, for example, ethylene.

The direction of a halogen atom mesomeric effect is the opposite to a halogen atom inductive effect. Thus the two effects work in opposition and the resulting change in π-ionization potential on going from $CH_2 = CH_2$ to $CH_2 = CHBr$ can be thought of as representing a balance between the two effects. The mesomeric effect can also be explained in terms of molecular orbital theory. The bromine 4p orbitals have energy comparable with the π_{C-C} orbital in the $CH_2 = CH$ — moiety and one of them also has the same symmetry and thus can be combined with the π_{C-C} orbitals in the usual LCAO-type way, to produce two vinyl bromide molecular orbitals. One of these orbitals will have an energy above that of the higher energy-combining orbital, the other will have an energy less than that of the lower energy-combining orbital (Fig. 4.4). The character of each resulting molecular orbital will be largely that of the interacting atomic or localized molecular orbital closest in energy to the resultant MO. Thus in the case of vinyl bromide, the highest occupied orbital (π' in Fig. 4.4) (lowest IP) will be predominantly C—C π-bonding, although it will have some C—Br antibonding character.

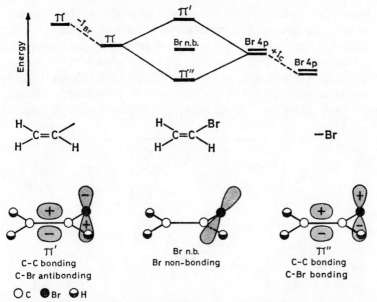

Fig. 4.4. Scheme for interactions of C—C—π and Br-4p lone pair orbitals in vinyl bromide.

In the molecule the energy of the π orbitals is lowered and that of the bromide 4p orbitals raised by inductive effects. One Br orbital does not interact with the π bond and remains non-bonding (Br-n.b.) One combination is bonding, π'', and mainly of Br character, the other is anti-bonding, and mainly of π character.

If no inductive effects were operating the difference between the energies of IPs of the π-orbitals in vinyl bromide and in ethylene could be thought of as a quantitative measure of the $+M$ effect associated with the substituent. However, as the $-I$, electron withdrawing, effect of the bromine will tend to increase the π'-orbital IP, the experimentally observed shift must be thought of as representing the combined $+M$ and $-I$ influences.

"LONE-PAIR" NON-BONDING ORBITALS AND INTERACTIONS BETWEEN THEM

Ionization from formal lone-pair orbitals within a molecule can give rise to sharp bands in photoelectron spectra. This is especially true if the orbitals are the outermost occupied orbitals of chlorine or bromine and the first bands in the spectra of the alkyl iodides (Fig. 4.5) are so sharp that in several cases they show spin-orbit splitting effects. Other "lone-pair" peaks can often be distinguished, e.g. oxygen (Fig. 4.6), nitrogen (Figs. 4.9 and 4.17), sulphur (Fig. 4.8) and phosphorus (Fig. 4.7), but these may be quite broad indicating the "lone pairs" are in fact involved to some extent in bonding

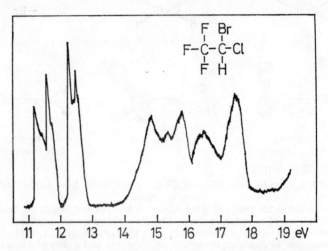

FIG. 4.5. UV-PE spectra of 1,1,1-trifluoro- 2-bromo- 2-chloroethane. (Bromine 4p in 11–12 eV, chlorine 3p in 12–13 eV and fluorine 2p in 14–17 eV regions respectively.) [13]

molecular orbitals. Fluorine-containing materials rarely show a fluorine "lone-pair" peak in their photoelectron spectra, since the F 2p orbital is invariably incorporated into bonding.

One interesting effect observed by photoelectron spectroscopy is the interaction across space of lone-pair orbitals. If any two such orbitals are close enough, have the same symmetry and comparable energy they can interact in just the same way as can any two atomic orbitals to give two molecular orbitals, one of lower energy than the energy of the least energetic of the two atomic orbitals and one of higher energy than the energy of the higher orbital. If the atomic

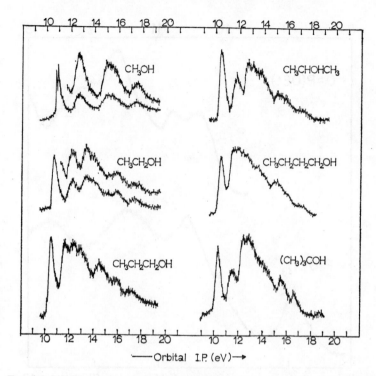

FIG. 4.6. UV-PE spectra of alcohols. (2p oxygen lone pair peaks in 10–11 eV region.)

orbitals are identical the energies of the two molecular orbitals will be symmetrically above and below the energy of the atomic orbitals. Formally, the molecular orbital of lower energy is a bonding orbital and the one of higher energy is an antibonding orbital. However, ionization would be from two non-equivalent orbitals and this should be reflected in the photoelectron spectrum. If the orbitals were too far apart to interact, or were of disparate energy or of different symmetry, there would be no interaction and the orbitals would be looked on as non-bonding, localized atomic orbitals. Thus, in a compound with two atoms with two occupied p-orbitals each, two of which could interact and two otherwise equivalent

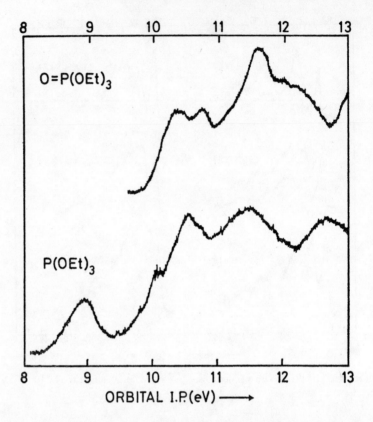

Fig. 4.7. UV-PE spectra of triethyl phosphate and triethyl phosphite. The phosphorus lone pair peak in the phosphite at 9 eV is broad, indicating that the orbital has appreciable bonding character. Oxygen lone pair peak in the phosphate is merged with the main bands of the spectrum, also indicating that the orbital has little non-bonding character.

ones which could not, one would expect to see three peaks on the intensity ratio 1:2:1. It is a simplified picture in so far as it ignores completely interactions with any other orbitals of the same symmetry, and similar energy.

The effect is clearly shown in the spectra of ethane thiols (Fig. 4.8). The first band in the spectrum of ethane thiol is due to ionization from the sulphur non-bonding 3p orbital. The band is clearly split in the dithiol spectrum indicating an interaction of the two S 3p atomic orbitals. Similar interactions are indicated by the spectra of several dichloroalkanes.[18] Bands in the 10·5–12·5 eV range are due to ionization from orbitals which are derived principally from atomic chlorine 3p orbitals. It is noticeable that there

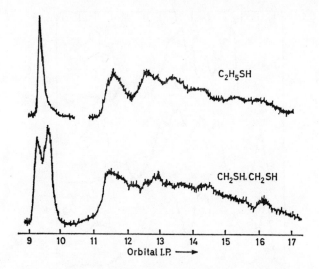

Fig. 4.8. UV-PE spectra of ethane thiol and 1,2-ethane dithiol. The sulphur 3p lone pair peak at ∼ 9·5 eV for the monothiol is split by interaction for the dithiol. Note relative areas of sulphur and alkyl bands provides help to distinguish between a mono and dithiol.

are no really sharp bands which might be labelled "chlorine lone pair". There are either two peaks or a single one of such width that it is indicative of an unresolved pair. As expected the magnitude of the "lone-pair" interaction, as measured by the separation of the "chlorine" bands, is greatest for 1,2-dichloropropane and least for 1,4-dichlorobutane. Two peaks are observed in the spectrum of the former at approximately 11·1 and 11·75 eV, and the width of the "chlorine" band is approximately 0·65 eV. The width of the "chlorine" band in 1,3-dichloropropane is approximately 0·9 eV, indicating some interaction. A more pronounced interaction is found in the spectrum of 1,4-diaza-bicyclo [2.2.2]octane, which has been examined by Heilbronner *et al.*[11] (Fig. 4.9). The splitting of the two nitrogen lone-pair orbitals, which interact across the ring, is 2·13 eV. The greater splitting probably reflects the greater ridigity of the ring compounds. The same paper also shows the spectra of the

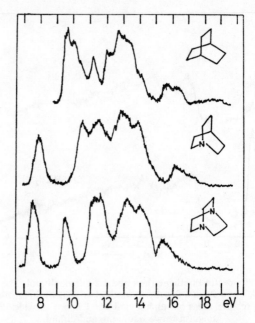

Fig. 4.9. UV-PE spectra of bicyclo [2.2.2]octane, quinuclidine and 1,4-di-aza-bicyclo [2.2.2]octane. The nitrogen lone pair bands are centred at $\sim$ 8eV. [11]

related quinuclidine and bicyclo [2.2.2]octane. The nitrogen lone-pair peak is very clear and the spectral shifts which result when nitrogen replaces carbon, which are expected on grounds of electronegativity, are also clearly shown. Interactions between dissimilar lone pairs, e.g. the oxygen and halogen lone pairs in ethylene halohydrins, have also been noted[8] (Fig. 4.10).

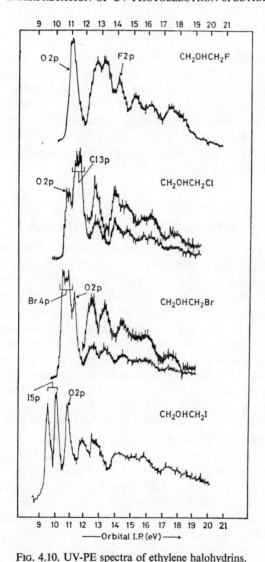

FIG. 4.10. UV-PE spectra of ethylene halohydrins.
The orbital energies decrease in the following order
$$F\ 2p > Cl\ 3p > C\ 2p > Br\ 4p > I\ 5p$$
so that the character of the highest energy molecular orbital formed by inter-action of the lone pair orbitals of O and Hal changes from being almost totally O 2p in the fluorohydrin to almost purely iodine-5p in the iodohydrin.

π-ORBITALS

Often the highest occupied orbital of an organic molecule is of π character. Thus the first peak in many spectra, at about 9 eV, is due to ionization from a π-orbital. The band shape is usually different from that associated with "lone-pair" ionization, being broader and having longer vibrational series. The interactions of π-orbitals with lone pair p-orbitals and other orbitals is of considerable chemical interest and the way in which interactions affect the PE spectra will now be dealt with.

INTERACTIONS BETWEEN π-SYSTEMS AND LONE-PAIR ORBITALS

If a non-bonding p-orbital in a molecule is sterically oriented so that it has the same symmetry as a π-orbital, is close enough to interact and the π- and p-orbitals are of comparable energy, interaction will take place. The interaction, as discussed earlier in this chapter, is responsible for the effect known as mesomerism. If the interaction is between a halogen lone-pair orbital and the π-orbital of a double bond, as in vinyl bromide, one of the two lone-pair orbitals has the wrong symmetry to interact with the π-orbital so that it remains non-bonding and serves as a "marker" in calculating the extent of interaction. Interaction can thus be looked on as effectively a splitting of the degeneracy of the two lone-pair halogen orbitals (Fig. 4.4). The process and the overall effect of inductive and mesomerism effects on the spectrum can also be seen in Fig. 4.4. The spectra of vinyl bromide is given in Fig. 4.11. The degree of interaction is much greater than that between comparable non-bonding orbitals such as dichloropropane, being typically of the order of 1–2 eV. The formation of a molecular orbital from two atomic orbitals involves some loss of "atomic" character. The degree of loss depends on the extent of mixing: in some spectra it is quite easy to recognize atomic character in spectral peaks, in others it is difficult. If the orbitals to be mixed have comparable energies and are able to overlap well, the characteristics of the interacting orbitals will be blended. If the energies are not very

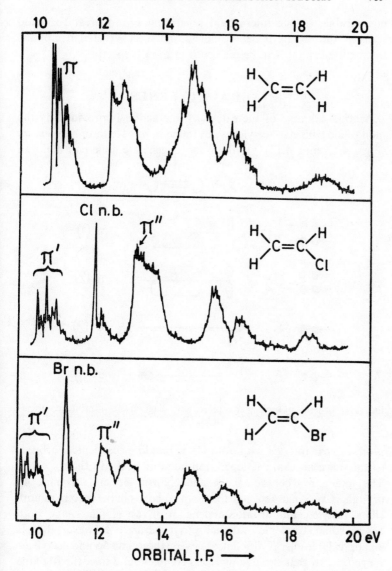

FIG. 4.11. UV-PE spectra of ethylene, vinyl chloride and vinyl bromide. Note how the halogen non-bonding lone pair peak serves as a marker.

comparable, or the interorbital separation is too great for good overlap, the mixing is less complete and the characteristics of the interacting orbitals can be discerned in the PE spectra.

HALOACETYLENES

A good example of the extent of interaction is provided by the mono-halogenated acetylenes examined by Heilbronner *et al.* (Figs. 4.12 and 4.13).[12] Both the degenerate lone-pair halogen

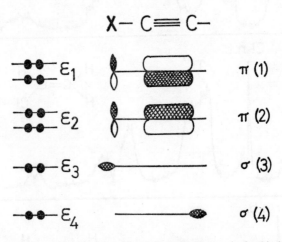

Fig. 4.12. Scheme of molecular orbital energy diagram and of orbital combinations.[12]

p-orbitals can interact with both C—C bonding acetylenic π orbitals so there are no sharp halogen non-bonding peaks in their spectra. The interaction between the π and chlorine 3p and bromine 4p orbitals is very marked and the first two bands in the spectra of both chloroacetylene and bromoacetylene are of very similar shape, both having some acetylenic π and halogen p character. However, there is an appreciable energy difference between the iodine 5p and acetylenic π-orbitals, so that the mixing is less complete, and since the IP of the iodine 5p is lower than the acetylene π the first orbital has pronounced iodine character, i.e. spin-orbit coupling. However, there is obviously

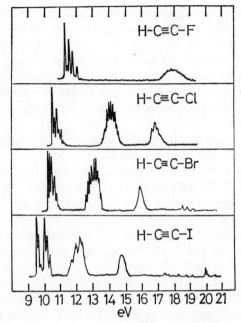

FIG. 4.13. UV-PE spectra of monohaloacetylenes.[12]

some degree of mixing because the second orbital also has clear signs of iodine character. The spectrum of fluoroacetylene is more difficult to interpret. The energy separation between acetylinic π and fluorine 2p orbitals is too great to allow much interaction, and consequently the first band in the spectrum of fluoroacetylene is virtually pure π. In general, it is much more difficult to detect the lone-pair IP of fluorine than those of the other halogens. In this compound it is probable that the broad peak at about 18 eV is due to the ionization of the fluorine lone pair (at 17·8 eV) and the σ_{C-H} bonding orbital is at 18 eV. The effect of decreasing electronegativity of the substituent halogen is noted in the shift of corresponding bands to lower IP.

These qualitative observations have been refined by Heilbronner et al.[12] into an elegant quantitative study of the spectra. With the aid of simple molecular orbital theory and spectral shifts they have calculated the appropriate resonance and coulomb integrals. Their argument is that used earlier in this chapter but is expressed in a more exact way. It can be put in an empirical form by saying that if two orbitals, which can be identified with an atom or group of ionization potentials IP_A and IP_B, give rise to two different orbitals with the ionization potentials IP_1 and IP_2 then $IP_A + IP_B = IP_1 + IP_2$.

This works quite well for the π-orbitals of the haloacteylenes. The π-orbital IP for acetylene is 11·40 eV (IP_A) and the first IPs (IP_B) of the halogen atoms from fluorine to iodine are, respectively, 17·42, 13·01, 11·84 and 10·45 eV. Since the first IP of chloroacetylene is 10·63 eV (IP_1) the IP of the associated orbital (IP_2) will be predicted to be 13·78 eV. The true value is 14·08 eV.

It is more difficult to apply to the σ-orbitals since IPs for the appropriate C-hal and C—H orbitals have to be assigned and it is not easy to isolate the C—C contribution to these orbitals. Nevertheless, an approximate value of 18 eV can be deduced from the spectrum of acetylene for the C—H orbital[12,13] and from the spectra of dihaloacetylenes[14] approximate values for C—I, C—Br and C—Cl σ IPs are 15·5, 16·9 and 17·8 eV. From these values and the value of the IP of the third band in the spectra of the monohaloacetylenes the IP of the fourth band can be calculated. The agreement is not very good (partly because we have simplified the argument). Nevertheless, even in this crude form, it provides a useful aid in the interpretation of spectra, if it is necessary to identify the origin of a peak.

Heilbronner *et al.*[97] have also applied their method to a series of dihaloacetylenes with success. In principle, it could be applied to many other compounds, but considerable care will be needed in selecting the values of IP_A and IP_B. It should usefully supplement the simple qualitative approach.

cis- AND *trans*-1,3-DICHLOROPROPENE

A careful analysis of the spectra of *cis*- and *trans*-1,3-dichloropropene illustrate two further points:

(i) How interaction of non-bonding p-orbitals can be superimposed on the interactions of non-bonding p and π-orbitals.

(ii) How peak areas can help to identify peaks in a spectrum.[14]

The shapes and positions of the peaks indicate the presence of chlorine "lone-pair" orbitals (Fig. 4.14). An interaction of some sort has clearly taken place because there are two fairly sharp peaks

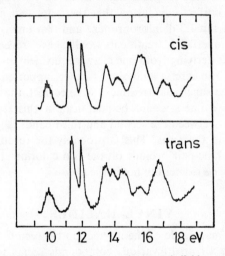

FIG. 4.14. UV-PE spectra of *cis-* and *trans-*1,3-dichloropropene.

present in this region, and such interaction might be expected since a "π"-band is observed at 10 eV. However, the relative areas of the two chlorine peaks at $\sim 11 \cdot 2$ eV and $\sim 11 \cdot 8$ eV suggest that there are twice as many electrons "under" the former than the latter. This therefore rules out the possibility of both peaks being derived from the splitting of two degenerate lone pair orbitals on one chlorine atom. It suggests that the peak of greatest area, $\sim 11 \cdot 2$ eV, derives from a chlorine atom which is not undergoing any interaction, and hence has a degenerate pair of orbitals upon it. This must be the —Cl atom of the —CH_2Cl group, and this implies that the peak at $11 \cdot 8$ eV derives from another chlorine atom which is interacting with the π-system, i.e. the Cl of the $CHCl{=}CH_2$— group. Such an interaction increases the "Cl 3p" IP (by withdrawing electronic charge from the chlorine atom or by stabilizing the chlorine orbitals by involving them in bond formation, depending on how you care to look at it) and also splits the two lone pair orbitals. The second one is then to be found under the 13·1 eV band (this is not immediately obvious but comparison of the spectra with those of vinyl halides and ethylene suggests that it is there). Thus careful analysis supports the correct conclusion that there are two non-equivalent chlorine atoms in 1,3-dichloropropene and that one is adjacent to a π-bond. A superficial treatment would have revealed just two chlorine peaks deriving from one or two equivalent atom(s) adjacent to a π-bond. The careful analysis is further supported by the reflection that if the superficial treatment were correct, the spectra of the *cis* and *trans* isomers would be identical in this region, whereas the separation between the second and third bands is greater for the *cis* isomer than the *trans*. This is probably the result of the interaction of the lone-pair orbitals on the two chlorine atoms, which is possible in the *cis* isomer but not in the *trans*.

VINYL HALIDES

The actual magnitude of the interaction between C—C π-orbitals and Cl 3p or Br 4p in various compounds seems to vary up to about 1·5 eV, but there has been controversy as to the precise splittings in specific compounds. Baker and Turner[15] concluded from a low-resolution spectrum of vinyl chloride that the "Cl 3p peaks" were split by about 1 eV. This result would have implied that the interaction between the π- and Cl 3p orbitals was greater in vinyl chloride than in chlorobenzene. Lake and Thompson[16] claimed, however, that a higher resolution spectrum showed peaks at 11·72 eV (observed earlier by Baker and Turner) and 11·87 eV (unresolved by Baker and Turner), and they suggested that these should be attributed to the perturbed and unperturbed "Cl 3p" orbitals thus giving a splitting of only 0·15 eV. They assigned the band at 13·0 eV to the highest occupied σ-level. We have further examined the high-resolution spectrum of vinyl chloride (Fig. 4.11), and by comparison of it with the spectra of the other vinyl halides,

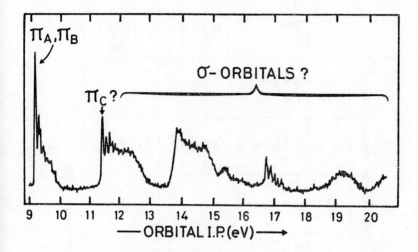

FIG. 4.15. UV-PE spectrum of benzene.

it seems that Baker and Turner's original interpretation was correct. The peak at 11·87 eV observed by Lake and Thompson is almost certainly part of a vibrational progression associated with the 11·72 eV IP. A count of the number of bands in the total photoelectron spectra of the vinyl halides further shows that the interpretation of Lake and Thompson would give more bands in the spectra than there were occupied orbitals, and it cannot therefore be correct.

SUBSTITUTED BENZENES

The first paper to note the interaction of lone-pair orbitals and π-orbitals was that by Baker, May and Turner on the PE spectra of benzene and substituted benzenes.[17] This paper contains, besides the ideas to be discussed below, the spectra of forty-three related compounds and shows that these are quite distinct. It also relates spectral characteristics with mesomeric and inductive effects of the substituents.

Benzene itself, by virtue of its symmetry, has been subjected to a number of molecular orbital calculations, the results of some of

TABLE 4.1. CALCULATED ORBITAL ENERGIES AND EXPERIMENTAL IONIZATION POTENTIALS FOR BENZENE*

Order and type of Orbitals[15]	$1e^2_{2g}$ σ	$2a^2_{1g}$ σ	$1b^2_{1u}$ σ	$1b^2_{2u}$ σ	$2e^4_{1u}$ σ	$1a^2_{2u}$ π	$2e^4_{2g}$ σ	$1e^4_{1g}$ π
Type	Weak C←→C Weak C—H	Weak C—C Strong C—H	C←→C Strong C—H	Strong C—C	Strong C—H	π Strong C—C	Weak C—C Weak C—H	Weak C—C π
Orbital—IP exptl[23]	19·0	16·8	15·4	14·7	13·9	12·4	11·7	9·2
Extended Huckel[19]	19·9	16·6	16·6	14·3	14·6	14·5	12·8	12·8
Gaussian LCAO-SCF[20]	19·4	15·5	15·3	12·2	13·0	12·3	10·2	7·8
Semi-Empirical SCF[21]	20·1	19·6	14·3	13·8	13·0	15·2	9·8	9·4
Semi-Empirical SCF[22]	—	—	—	—	—	15·6	—	8·3
Assignment of fine str. of photoelectron band		ν_2 ring breathing ν_1 C—H						ν_2 C_6 ring breathing ν_{18}

* Assignments follow Asbrink et al.,[18] for discussion of other interpretations see ref. 23.

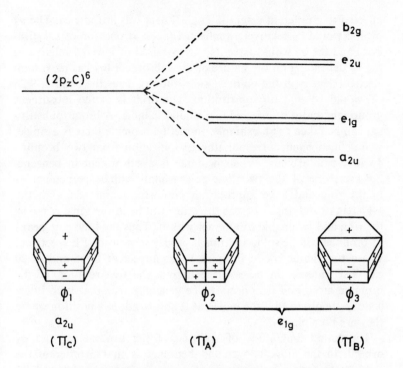

$(2p_zC)^6$

b_{2g}

e_{2u}

e_{1g}

a_{2u}

ϕ_1 ϕ_2 ϕ_3

a_{2u} e_{1g}

(π_C) (π_A) (π_B)

FIG. 4.16. Scheme of molecular orbital energy diagram and orbital combinations
for π orbitals of benzene.
In text it is assumed that substitution occurs on the atom in the extreme left or
right position of the ring as shown, i.e. a nodal position for ϕ_3, π_B.

which are shown in Table 4.1. Its photoelectron spectrum is shown
in Fig. 4.15. The experimental values of the ionization potentials
and the orbital assignments are also included in Table 4.1. The
orbital assignments are in fact a matter of some controversy, but
we include here the assignment which fits best the experimental
and theoretical results. The important region from the point of view
of substituent effects is 9–12 eV. In benzene itself there is no band
in the region 9·8–11·2 and the IP 9·25 eV band is assigned to the
degenerate π_2^b and π_3^b orbitals, whose forms are shown in Fig. 4.16.
These orbitals have a different spatial orientation and would be

affected to a different extent if a substituent was introduced. The π_2 orbital would be relatively unaffected (node at position of substitution) and the π_3 would have its energy raised or lowered relative to the π_2 depending on the nature of the substituent (π_3 has maximum electron density at the point of substitution). Thus the band at 9·25 eV would be split on substitution. The orbitals of the substituent group might also be affected in a similar manner. A bromo substituent can be taken as an example. In methyl bromide there is a single, well-defined band corresponding to ionization from two bromine 4p lone-pair orbitals. When bromine is a substituent in benzene, however, one of the two lone-pair orbitals will be perpendicular to the ring and have appropriate symmetry to interact with the π-system of the ring, whereas the other will be in the same plane as the ring and be unable to interact with it. Thus the lone-pair peaks of bromine will be split, and this is clearly seen in the PE spectrum, where the characteristic bromine peaks appear at 10·65 and 11·20 eV. This interaction takes place despite the free rotation of the bromine atom and it appears to be generally true that such interactions are observed if the molecule is able to adopt a position where they are possible.

The actual magnitude of splitting of the benzene π_2 and π_3 orbitals in the monohalogenated benzenes is in the order of the $+M$, mesomeric effects associated with halogens, and thus reflects the ability of the lone-pair electrons to increase the charge in the π_3 orbital. Examples of spectra of monosubstituted benzenes are shown in Fig. 4.17. Substituents which are able to remove charge from the π-orbitals by inductive effect, $-I$, e.g. $-CF_3$, do not split the benzene π_2 and π_3 orbitals. There is a linear correlation between the mean IP of π_2 and π_3 in substituted benzenes and the rate of reaction of these compounds with CF_3 showing that the mean πIP is a reasonable measure of electron density. With 1,4-disubstituted benzenes the splitting was the sum of splittings brought about by the individual substituent groups in mono-substituted benzene, unless the splitting caused by one group, e.g. $-Br$, $-OMe$, was very great.

The other effect to be observed is the shifting of the π-levels on alteration of the substituent group. In general an electronegative

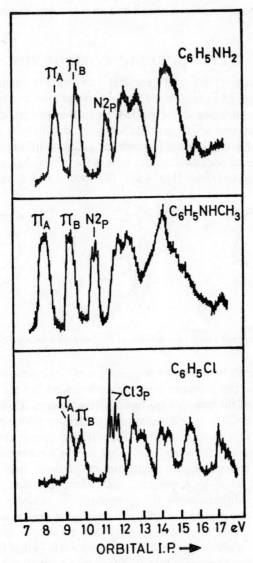

FIG. 4.17. UV-PE spectra of substituted benzene.
Note the splitting of the π_A and π_B orbitals and the chlorine 3p orbitals. The
nitrogen 2p lone pair peaks are also seen.[17]

group will tend to increase the IP and an electropositive one decrease it.

HETEROCYCLIC COMPOUNDS

The arguments which are applicable to benzene cannot so obviously be applied to substituted five-membered aromatic heterocycles but they do provide useful guide-lines in the interpretation of the spectra. The two upper π-orbitals are not degenerate; one orbital has a nodal plane passing through the heteroatom, the other has a nodal plane perpendicular to this so that the orbital has pronounced heteroatomic character (Fig. 4.18). The spectra of the unsubstituted

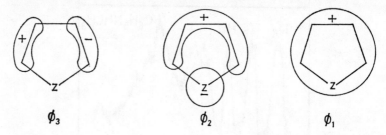

FIG. 4.18. Occupied π molecular orbitals of 5-membered heterocyclic compounds.

five-membered heterocycles containing only one heteroatom (Fig. 4.19) reflect the differences in the heteroatoms by the degree of separation of the first two (π) bands of the spectra. This separation reflects the ability of the heteroatom's outermost p lone-pair orbital to interact with C—C π-orbitals. There is no evidence in the spectra of "lone pairs" of electrons localized on the heteroatom, i.e. the system is truly aromatic. Substitution patterns are also more difficult to relate to mesomeric and inductive effects. There are pronounced differences in the spectra of, for example, 2- and 3-substituted thiophenes, and different substituent groups bring about shifts in the positions of the bands in the spectra. Thus from a qualitative viewpoint the situation is very similar to that for benzene and substituted benzenes, but it is less easy to explain the various shifts in the absence of complete MO treatments of the molecules.

Some heterocyclic molecules contain heteroatoms with outer shell p-lone pairs which have the wrong symmetry to enter into the aromatic π-system. In this class fall the nitrogen 2p orbitals of pyridine and of isoxazole, and one of the two nitrogen 2p orbitals of pyrazole. The magnitudes of the two upper π-orbitals and the N 2p lone-pair orbital ionization potentials in these compounds have been calculated and found to be similar. The relevant orbital ionization potentials are given by the first three bands in the photoelectron spectra. The question as to which of the three bands relates to the π-orbitals and which to the "lone-pair" orbitals is answered by comparing the spectra of similar compounds. For example, the first two bands in the spectrum of pyrrole are centred at 8·2 eV and 9·2 eV. These relate to the π_3 and π_2 orbitals, which have the symmetries shown in Fig. 4.18. Replacement of the α-carbon of pyrrole by nitrogen leads to the compound pyrazole. Since the new nitrogen atom is more electronegative than carbon and is in a region of high electron density with respect to both the π_3 and π_2 orbitals, it would be expected to have the effect of making the π_3 and π_2 orbitals IP greater in pyrazole than in pyrrole. The first IP of pyrazole is 9·5 eV, and the raising is thus 1·3 eV. If we assume that the second π IP were raised by a similar amount, then the bond centred at 10·8 eV in the pyrazole spectrum would have to be assigned to π_2. This would give the 10·1-eV band as "N2p".[24]

STERIC EFFECTS

It is to be expected that mesomeric effects, which depend on overlapping of p- and π-orbitals, will be inhibited if steric considerations prevent overlap.[25] An example is provided by the series phenol (PhOH), anisole (PhOCH$_3$) and t-butoxybenzene (PhOC(CH$_3$)$_3$) in which the splitting of the benzene π_2 and π_3 bands is 0·70, 0·83 and 0·60 eV, respectively.[17] The —OCH$_3$ group which is electron donating increases the band separation, by stabilizing π_2 relative to π_3. The —OC(CH$_3$) group which is even more electron donating does not split the orbitals to the same degree. This is because the p–π interaction is via the p-orbitals of the oxygen, and in order to accommodate the t-butyl group this oxygen p-orbital is twisted out

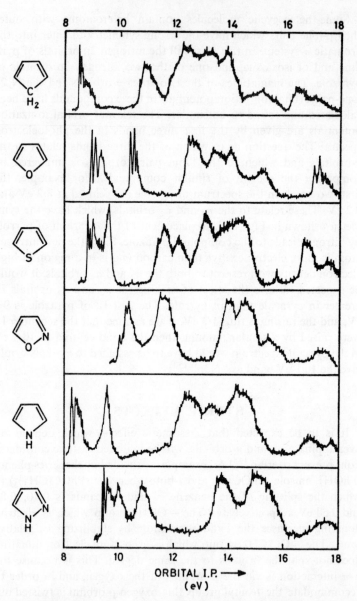

FIG. 4.19. UV-PE spectra of various 5-membered heterocyclic compounds. Note how position and the splitting of the π bands in the region 8–11 eV is influenced by changes in the electronegativity of the heteroatom.

of alignment with the benzene π-orbitals. It is certain that more examples of this effect will become known in the future.

The interaction between the two ethylenic groups in $F_2C:CF$ $CF:CF_2$ is only one-third of that found for both butadiene and $F_2C:C$ $HCH:CF_2$.[26] Thus in order to accommodate the fluorine atoms in $F_2C:CF$ $CF:CF_2$ the carbon skeleton is forced into a non-planar configuration.

THE PERFLUORO EFFECT

The effect of substituting hydrogen or other atoms within a molecule by fluorine leads in general to an increase in IP of most of the orbitals, because of the high electronegativity of (or strong inductive effect exerted by) fluorine. In several aliphatic molecules, however, the effect is to increase the IPs of σ-orbitals but not the π-orbitals, e.g. H_2O, F_2O; $H_2C=CH_2$, $F_2C=CF_2$; H_2CO, F_2CO.[27] Fluorination then serves to identify the σ- and π-orbitals. The situation, which is discussed by Brundle and Robin,[26] is less clear for aromatic compounds, in which both π- and σ-orbitals are affected by fluorine substitution.

CORRELATIONS

It would be convenient to have correlation diagrams and "group IPs" of the sort that are used in IR and NMR spectroscopy. Correlation diagrams can be drawn up (Figs. 6.7 and 6.8) and are useful for identification of compounds. They also show how particular IPs shift in a related series of compounds and underline the changes which take place at IPs higher than have been discussed above.

It is impossible to be absolute about correlations, because one is concerned with molecular orbital energies and a C—O type orbital may be very similar to a C—C or a C—Cl type orbital, because the atomic orbitals have similar energies and symmetry. This is of course analogous to the difficulty in IR of distinguishing between C=C, C=N and C=O frequencies. Further splittings due to orbital interactions may be considerable. Nevertheless, some guidelines can be laid down and they are marked in Figs. 6.7 and 6.8.

Broadly speaking IPs increase in the order: lone-pairs of I, S, P

< aromatic π (usually two to three associated peaks) $\sim \pi$ aliphatic < lone pairs of Br, Cl, O, N < σ_p C—O, C—Cl, C—C < lone-pair F < σ_s.

In making correlations band shapes and fine structures are usually of paramount importance.

FUTURE DEVELOPMENTS AND OTHER STUDIES

The treatment above has been pedagogic in intent. There is in fact a great deal of work to be done before UV–PE spectra are properly understood. Little is known at present about peak intensities or orbital ionization cross-sectional areas. Secondary reactions in the target chamber almost certainly take place and these can result in slightly different spectra being obtained for the same compound under different operating conditions. Scarcely any attempt has been made to identify σ-orbitals of high (15–20 eV) IP and to correlate spectral shifts with molecular properties. There is also an obvious need for improved MO calculations. These problems are being investigated and preliminary results are being reported at conferences, but at this stage we feel there is insufficient evidence to warrant discussion in this review.

The examples discussed above are representative and have been chosen purely for their illustrative value. For a different viewpoint the reviews of Brundle and Robin,[28] Price,[29,30] Baker,[31] Brundle,[32] Turner[33-35] and Berry[36] can be consulted. Price, as a physicist, who has made extremely influential contributions to the development of the technique, presents ideas in a way that is both different and stimulating to the chemist. Turner's views are given more space in the book by him and his co-workers,[13] which is the first major work for anyone at all interested in the topic. It contains the spectra of many compounds and discusses them in detail, especially inert gases, di and tri atomic molecules, formaldehyde, formamides, etc., aliphatic hydrocarbon, three-membered ring compounds, alkyl and alkenyl halides, acrolein, benzene and substituted benzenes, heterocyclic aromatic compounds, cyamides and a few inorganic compounds.

REVIEW OF OTHER STUDIES

The number of compounds whose spectra are being reported is increasing rapidly. Many of these reports appear in journals, which are unfamiliar to many chemists, but a good title-abstracting service is provided by the *Bulletin for Mass Spectrometry*. The following is a brief survey of the papers published up to mid-1971. Many of them are concerned with relatively small molecules which are susceptible to both experimental and theoretical studies, so that they are of considerable interest to those wishing to understand the basic principles of photoelectron spectroscopy.

Diatomic and triatomic compounds

The work of Turner's group is well represented in their book.[13] Individual papers which serve to illustrate the principles of their approach are the studies of hydrogen and oxygen,[37] water and deuterium oxide,[38] the measurement of Frank–Condon factors, i.e. the detailed study of fine structure of H_2, CO, O_2, NO,[39] CO_2, COS, CS_2 and N_2O[40] and the high resolution spectra of N_2O, COS, CS_2 and CO_2.[41] These molecules have also been studied by other workers. Collin and Natalis have obtained the spectrum of NO[42] and CO_2, COS and CS_2,[43] and Eland and Danby have investigated CO_2, CS_2 and SO_2 and used the results to calculate the bond angle in SO_2^+.[44] Comparison of these studies by three independent groups reveals the differences in resolution which are obtainable by different instruments, and the question of whether all the peaks observed in photoelectron spectra are due to direct ionization is clearly raised by Collin and Natalis. They have pressed this important point on a number of occasions and it will be mentioned again below. The higher IPs of nitric oxide have been determined by Samson,[45] and Brundle has investigated the first IP and that of nitrogen dioxide with an argon resonance line source.[46]

It is obviously of interest to relate photoelectron spectra with results from other spectroscopic techniques, which involve ionization such as mass spectrometry and UV electronic spectroscopy. Lindholm's group has embarked upon a series of such studies, the smallest molecules examined being O_2, N_2 and CO.[47] The most complete study to date is that of nitrogen dioxide by Brundle et al.[48] The PE spectra were obtained with both He(I) (584 A) and He(II) (304 A), two extra bands corresponding to orbitals with IPs between 21 and 41 eV being observed with the latter. The PE and vacuum UV spectroscopic results were found to interrelate well and much more could be interpreted by a combination of the techniques than from each alone. The band shapes of the PE spectrum, in particular, are elucidated by a knowledge of the excited states associated with each band. The fragmentation process revealed by the mass spectrum of nitrogen dioxide is also usefully correlated with the PE spectrum. Finally, the authors have carried out SCF molecular orbital energy calculations. The agreement between the theoretical and experimental IPs is within 2 eV for all but the first for which the discrepancy is 5 eV. They have also drawn up a correlation diagram of the PE spectra of other bent triatomic molecules N_2O, CO_2, O_3, SO_2 and CF_2 which shows how the orbital energies vary between the compounds. It is of interest from the analytical viewpoint that the presence of an estimated 2% of nitric oxide was detected although the nitrogen dioxide was claimed at least 99·9% pure.

Inorganic halides

The halogens and halogen acids have been studied by Frost et al.[49] Price et al., who have made a thorough investigation of the spectra of the halogen acids,[50] agree with most of the interpretation of Frost et al., but show their interpretation of the hydrofluoric acid spectra to be in error.[51] Price had thoroughly investigated the ionization of first-row hydrides as well as fluorides before the advent of photoelectron spectroscopy[52] and his earlier conclusions have been elaborated as a result of his application of PES.[30,53] The hydrides can be treated by the united-atom approach[54] in which the hydrides isoelectronic with the next inert gas are considered to be distorted inert gas atoms. For example, hydrogen chloride is considered as argon atom from which a nucleus and an electron have been partly withdrawn. Price demonstrates how this can lead to a satisfactory interpretation of the photoelectron spectra. The approach has limited applicability, but nevertheless, it is a very healthy reminder both that a simple approach gives the right answer and that there is more than one useful model of bonding.

The boron halides and hydrides have been carefully studied, notably by Lloyd's group and that of Frost and McDowell. They include BF_3,[55,56] BCl_3 and BBr_3,[56] B_2H_6,[56] borazine[58] and related compounds.[59] The symmetry of these compounds allows the molecular orbital energy diagram to be constructed both qualitatively and quantitatively.[55–59,61,62] The non-equivalence of molecular orbitals from the halogen lone-pair orbitals is clearly reflected in the spectra. The interpretations of these are not always in agreement with each other or the predictions of INDO and CNDO/2 calculations, but the arguments employed are urgently expressed and every facet of the spectrum is taken into account. The diborane ion has also been considered by Rose et al.[61,62]

The spectrum of carbon tetrafluoride has been reported by the same groups[63–65] and by Manne.[66] Lloyd has also discussed the spectra of SF_6, SeF_6 and TeF_6 obtained with a low-resolution grid instrument.[67] Better spectra of sulphur hexafluoride have been reported.[13,68,69] Spectra obtained by the ionization of xenon difluoride with He(I) and He(II) radiation are essentially in accord with molecular orbital predictions.[70] The halogen cyanides ClCN, BrCN and ICN can be contrasted with monohaloacetylenes.[12] The overlapping of halogen p-orbitals with the cyanide π-orbitals similarly leads to the formation of molecular orbitals, which are clearly identifiable in the spectrum.[71] The question of whether or not there is p $\rightarrow$ d π-bonding in silanes and germanes has been settled by Cradock and Ebsworth,[72] who have obtained the spectra of SiH_3Cl and GeH_3Cl. Compared with CH_3Cl the chlorine lone pair band is much broader and its position does not agree with predictions based solely on electronegativity. These facts are in accord with the view that the orbital from which ionization is taking place is bonding.

Inorganic nitrogen and phosphorus compounds

Ammonia and phosphine were naturally examined by the early workers,[13] but the most satisfactory study is probably that of

Frost and McDowell *et al.* who have also examined ND_3 and have compared the experimental results with those obtained theoretically by INDO and CNDO/2 calculations.[73] The INDO approach proved more successful but neither was particularly accurate in its predictions. The spectrum of ammonia proves that there are exceptions to the generalizations made above. The "lone-pair" peak is

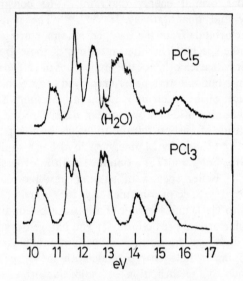

FIG. 4.20. UV-PE spectra of PCl_3 and PCl_5.

far from being sharp. It has a half-width of approximately 0·75 eV and has fifteen clearly resolvable vibrational peaks as fine structure. The reason for this is that ionization of the electron in lone-pair orbital leads to a flattening of the molecule with consequent change of symmetry and vibrational frequency. In other words, the basic premise that ejection of the "lone-pair" electron does not affect the molecule is again not met. For the same reason ammonia falls off the frequency correlation graph proposed by Turner.[74] The spectra of phosphine and arsine are similar to that of ammonia but shifted to lower IP.[75]

The symmetry of the molecule also influences the spectra of nitrogen and phosphorus halides, because the bands due to the halogen "lone-pair" electrons are split in a distinctive manner (Fig. 4.20). In a tetrahedral molecule they split into a- and t-type orbitals, with an intensity ratio of $1:3$ respectively and in a molecule with C_{3v} symmetry they split into a and e-type orbitals with intensity ratios of $1:2$. The actual number of filled orbitals and the order of filling varies from molecule to molecule, and the band intensity ratios are so far as the spectra are concerned only approximate, but the pattern of splitting of non-bonding orbitals is characteristic of a molecule. For example, in PBr_3 there are six bromine 4-p lone-pair orbitals, which give rise to four bands in the PE spectrum 2 a-type and 2 e-type. The chlorine- and bromine- containing compounds generally give rise to a group of sharp peaks in the region 10–12 eV.

The spectra of NF_3 and NOF_3 have been obtained by Bassett and Lloyd[64] and that of NCl_3 by Price.[76] Bassett and Lloyd have also examined PF_3 and POF_3[77] in conjunction with the theoreticians Hillier and Saunders, who have also correlated the spectra of PCl_3 and $POCl_3$[78] and PH_3, PF_3, $(CH_3)_3P$[79] with IPs calculated by *ab initio* calculations. They show that the highest occupied orbital is a non-bonding one of mainly 3-p character and that there is a significant degree of p–d π-bonding, especially in PF_3. The agreement between the theoretically derived and experimental values is quite good.

The spectra of isocyamic acid and related compounds has been profitably compared with those of simple compounds containing carbon, nitrogen, oxygen and sulphur by Eland.[80]

Organometallic compounds

The spectrum of mercury[81,82] has been obtained and so have the spectra of relatively volatile organomercury compounds notably methyl and dimethyl mercury.[83] The latter are quite characteristic. The dimethyl zinc and cadmium have additionally been examined by Distefano and Diebeler.[84] Several other organometallic compounds have been subjected to examination by photoelectron spectroscopy and the results are in accord with predictions made by ligand field theory. In fact, from the pedagogic viewpoint the splitting of d-orbitals is very satisfactorily demonstrated in several photoelectron spectra. Turner *et al.* carried out an early study on ferrocene,[13] and since then Lloyd and Schlag have studied iron and nickel carbonyls and nitrosyl carbonyls, comparing the results with those from photoionization spectroscopy.[85] Green *et al.* have given a detailed account of the spectra of manganese pentacarbonyl derivatives[86] and vanadium hexacarbonyl[87] and Green *et al.* have obtained spectra of trifluorophosphine, $Ni(PF_3)_4$ and $Pt(PF_3)_4$.[88] The volatile chlorides of titanium and vanadium have been examined by Lloyd.[89]

Studies of inorganic compounds which presage future developments are the study by Bordass and Linnett of species adsorbed on the surface of a metal,[90] and the spectra of NaI, MgI and TlI obtained at high temperatures by Berkowitz and Chupka[91] and TlI by Ridyard.[92] The reported spectra were not good but refinements in technique can be expected to lead to improved spectra. The spectra of the iodides were obtained by injecting the sample as a molecular beam. The procedure contaminates the apparatus but Berkowitz[93] is currently engaged in designing better beams, sample injection systems and detectors so that obtaining spectra of samples in the form of a molecular beam could become a viable routine method. This would allow solid samples to be introduced. It is possible that the lack of fine structure in the spectra and the broad bands are consequences of high temperature at which the spectra were obtained. Then the molecular ion would be so excited that the lower vibrational levels would not be occupied and it is possible that the parent molecule is also excited to some extent so that $v_1 \rightarrow v_n$ as well as $v_0 \rightarrow v_n$ transitions take place (cf. Chapter 3).

Aliphatic compounds

The simpler organic molecules are dealt with at length by Turner *et al.*[13] A paper from the same group, which demonstrates their interpretive approach very well is the one on methane, ethane, ethylene and formaldehyde.[94] The spectra of these molecules between them illustrate the resolution of fine structure into several vibrational series, Jahn–Teller splitting and the correlation of bands with molecular orbitals and calculated molecular orbital energies as well as providing spectra which are basic to the understanding of alkyl and ethylenic derivatives. The chlorinated, fluorinated and mixed chlorinated and fluorinated ethylenes have been examined by Lake and Thompson.[16] We give above reasons for doubting the interpretation of the spectrum of vinyl chloride, but not withstanding this, the paper presents lucidly and simply a good account of the spectra of these compounds. The same authors have also examined simple compounds containing the cyanide group.[95] Dichloro-ethylenes have been discussed by Jonathan et al.[96] The work of Heilbronner et al. on the monohalogenated acetylenes has already been discussed. Similar arguments are used to explain the spectra of the dihalogen acetylenes.[97] Acetylene has been examined by Collin and Delwiche[98] and by Baker and Turner, who also reported on aza-acetylenes.[99] Frost et al. have compared methyl cyanide and methyl acetylene with results of SCF molecular orbital calculations.[100]

Cyclic compounds have been considered by several workers from the experimental and theoretical viewpoints. As part of a larger study of the optical spectra of small rings, Basch et al. have recorded and discussed the photoelectron spectra of cyclopropane, ethylene oxide and ethylenimine.[101] Dewar et al. have carried out a massive study of a large number of organic compounds[102] including cyclic hydrocarbons[103] and unsaturated polycyclic hydrocarbons.[104] The spectra have been at low resolution but the results have been interpreted with the aid of MINDO calculations, which have proved generally satisfactory. Worley has also commented on the IP of cyclobutadiene.[105] He and Dewar had previously dealt with cis 1,3-butadiene.[106]

The IPs of the halomethanes have been determined by Regle et al.,[107] and those of eight alkyl bromides have been measured by Hashmall and Heilbronner.[108] It was found by the latter workers that for a given number of carbon atoms in the alkyl group chain branching at the α-position lowered the IP by 0·2 eV whereas that at the β-position only lowered it by 0·09 eV. Alkyl halides, as well as alcohols and ethylene halohydrins, have been investigated by us, with emphasis on the analytical aspects of the method.[8] Brailsford and Ford have calculated the IPs of linear alkanes[109] and the spectra have been interpreted simply by Baker et al.[110]

The electronic structures of ethylene and diborane as calculated by theory and deduced from the photoelectron spectra have been thoroughly dealt with by Brundle et al.[111] From a briefer study of trivinyl boron it has been concluded that there is only a limited degree of conjugation through the boron.[112]

Aromatic and polycyclic compounds

Eland and Danby have compared the results obtained by photo-electron spectroscopy with those from an electron impact method for naphthalene, azulene, biphenyl and triphenylene.[113] The spectra of azulene and biphenyl were obtained under low resolution because of the involatility of these compounds. Those of indene and naphthalene are of much higher resolution, so a comparison of these spectra clearly shows the influence of slit width. The IPs agreed well with those calculated from Huckel theory, but this is not always the case for aromatic heteromolecules investigated by Eland. Nevertheless Eland shows that the theory is useful for the interpretation of the spectra of ethylene, butadiene, cyclo-octatriene, biphenylene, pyrrole, furan, thiophene, indole, benzofuran, thionaphthene, dibenzofuran, diphenyl ether, pyridine and pyrazine. The agreement is best with the aromatic hydrocarbons and the vertical IPs of the π-orbitals are given by the equation

$$IP = (6{\cdot}37 \mp 0{\cdot}12) + m\,(2{\cdot}70 \mp 0{\cdot}11)\ eV,$$

where m is Huckel theory coefficient, i.e. a root of the appropriate secular determinant. When hetero atoms or terminal $=CH_2$ groups are present the equation has to be modified. Reasonable assumptions result in similar linear equations for the IP, but the fit is less good and for sulphur containing compounds is poor. One conclusion which is drawn is that the IP of the highest occupied σ-band is close to $11{\cdot}5$ eV. Some fifteen five-membered heterocycles and substituted heterocycles have been examined from the analytical viewpoint.[115] The spectra are all qualitatively distinct and there are pronounced differences in the spectra of isomers such as 2-bromo- and 3-bromo-thiophene or 2-methyl and 3-methyl-thiophene. The mass spectra of the bromo derivatives are almost identical so it would clearly be advantageous to have a photoelectron spectrometer as a monitor of a GLC column, if the sensitivity of the method would allow it. The question of order of IPs in heterocyclic aromatic compounds has been examined by several authors.[24, 116,118] The IPs of the π and the n (lone pair nitrogen) orbitals are lower than the highest filled σ-orbital and the order is often π, n, σ. From the practical point of view, these studies show that care is needed in identifying bands due to lone-pair n nitrogen orbitals in a heterocyclic aromatic system since they may be very close to a π-band. Pyridine has also been examined by Goffart et al.[118] and by Jonnson et al., who also employed other techniques to support their interpretation.[119] Dewar et al. have also examined azabenzenes, azanaphthalenes[122] and fluorinated benzenes.[120]

Interactions of non-bonding orbitals

The interactions of lone pairs of electrons has already been discussed.[8,10] Heilbronner et al. have investigated the phenomenon in depth and shown interactions between non-conjugate π-bonds in 1,4-cyclo hexadiene, norbornadiene and bicyclo [2.2.2]octadiene,[122–3] 1,4,5,8-tetrahydronaphthalene[124] and between nitrogen lone pairs in trans-azomethane,[125] which has been compared with interactions in trans-2-butene and trans-acetaldehyde methylimin,[126] and in 1,4-diazabicyclo [2.2.2]octane.[127] All of these papers are very clearly presented and have considerable implications for analytical chemists. It is shown that there are "through bond" as well as "through space" interactions between orbitals of appropriate symmetry but separated by several atoms.

Errors

Baker et al.[128] have discussed the errors which may result from lack of experimental care or by application of false theory. They discussed the hypothesis proposed by Momigny et al.[129] that some occupied molecular orbitals were undetected by photoelectron spectroscopy, and found no evidence for it. Other issues at stake were the consistency of spectra excited by different sources, correlation with results from photon-impact studies, and comparisons of spectra with MO calculations. Another point of entry to a similar controversy is provided by Natalis et al.[130]

REVIEW OF OTHER STUDIES— ADDITIONAL MATERIAL

The field is rapidly expanding and since the above survey was concluded a number of relevant publications have appeared. They are noted below.

Further reviews have been provided by Turner[74,131] and Dormstadt.[132]

Additional studies of small molecules have been carried out, and our understanding of the technique has been advanced by them. Rotational fine structure has been found in the PE spectrum of hydrogen.[133] The PE spectra of several diatomic molecules have been compared with Penning ionization spectra.[134] In simple PE spectra the fine structure has been shown to be independent of the angle between incident photon beam and detector unless the excitation route is via an autoionization process.[135] The spectra of H, N and O atoms have been obtained.[136] More detailed studies of HF and DF,[137] nitric oxide[138] and hydrogen sulphide and selenide[139] have been reported. The interpretation offered by the authors of this last mentioned study was criticised when it was presented at a conference and it seems probable that it will be the starting point of another controversy.

The spectra of vanadium and titanium tetrachlorides have been obtained and interpreted[140] and the halides of group IV and IVA have been subjected to examination by several groups.[141–143] Some good spectra have been obtained during the studies and these have allowed scope for discussions on the ordering of orbitals and the extent of involvement of silicon d-orbitals in bonding. The ordering of orbitals in borazine has been contrasted with that in benzene[144] and the spectrum of trimethyl borazine has been obtained and interpreted.[145] From the spectrum of trivinylboron it has been argued that there is limited conjugation through boron.[146]

Lloyd and Lynaugh have obtained the spectra of the addition

compounds NH_3BH_3 and BH_3CO.[147] They differ appreciably from their components and suggest that reactions in the target chamber could give rise to spurious results (although in this study the compounds were first prepared and then admitted to the spectrometer).

Lloyd has also drawn attention to the fact that electron impact (EI) studies sometimes give the 2nd IP and not the 1st, so that caution is needed when comparing the results from PES and EI.[148]

Further confirmation of the relationship between IPs and Taft σ^* values is provided by Cocksey et al.[149]

Various methyl, phenyl and benzyl substituted hydrazines and amines have been studied by Dewar's group.[150] They relate IPs with ΔH_f. Their spectra are obtained with a retarding grid instrument and thus provide an interesting contrast with the more common form of spectra.

Bicyclic and exocyclic olefins have been examined by Demes and Yencha.[151] Haselbach has dealt with the Jahn-Teller splitting in cyclopropane on both theoretical and experimental grounds.[152] This is a prelude to the work of Heilbronner's group on cyclobutane,[153] cycloalkanes and alkenes[154] and the interaction of the Walsh e-type orbitals of cyclopropane with π-orbitals in bullvalenes,[155] fulvenes,[156] and related systems. As well as containing discussions of unusual and interesting compounds these papers present arguments, which encourage the belief that simplified interpretations of the spectra of complex compounds are both possible and valid.

The question of homoconjugation has also been discussed by the same group[157] and they have extended their studies on interactions of non-bonding electrons to dimethyl diazine[158] and pyrriadine pyridazine and pyrazine.[159] Pignataro et al. have claimed that the PE spectra of molecules having classically non-conjugated π-systems such as diphenylmethane, biphenyl and [2,2]-paracyclophane show evidence of through space interactions of the conjugated parts of the molecule.[160] The splitting of the benzene-type π-orbitals in these compounds is similar to that in toluene.

Heilbronner et al. have discussed the concept of homoaromaticity[161] and Hoffman has dealt with the paradoxical question of why electrons which should be delocalized can be thought of as localized.[162]

For analytical work and for the full interpretation of spectra it is desirable to know how to relate peak intensity to molecular and electronic parameters. Two theoretical studies have dealt with this difficult problem with some success.[163,164]

REFERENCES

1. A. D. BAKER, D. BETTERIDGE, N. R. KEMP and R. E. KIRBY, *Int. J. Mass Spec. Ion Phys.*, 1970, **4**, 90.
2. J. HINZE and H. H. JAFFE, *J. Amer. Chem. Soc.*, 1962, **84**, 540.
3. J. HINZE and H. H. JAFFE, *J. Amer. Chem. Soc.*, 1963, **85**, 148.
4. R. RICH, *Periodic Correlations*, Benjamin, New York, 1965, Chap. 3.
5. R. T. SANDERSON, *Inorganic Chemistry*, Reinhold, New York.
6. D. W. TURNER, *Adv. Phys. Org. Chem.*, 1966, **4**, 31.
7. R. W. TAFT in *Steric Effects in Organic Chemistry* (M. S. NEWMAN, Ed.), Wiley, New York, 1956, p. 619.
8. A. D. BAKER, D. BETTERIDGE, N. R. KEMP and R. E. KIRBY, *Anal. Chem.*, 1971, **43**, 375.
9. B. J. COCKSEY, J. H. D. ELAND and C. J. DANBY, *J. Chem. Soc.* (B), 1971, 790.
10. A. D. BAKER, D. BETTERIDGE and N. R. KEMP, unpublished results.
11. P. BISCHOF, J. A. HASHMALL, E. HEILBRONNER and V. HORNUNG, *Tetrahedron Letters*, 1969, **4025**.
12. H. J. HAINK, E. HEILBRONNER, V. HORNUNG and ELSE KLOSTER JENSEN, *Helv. Chim. Acta*, 1970, **53**, 1073.
13. D. W. TURNER, C. BAKER, A. D. BAKER and C. R. BRUNDLE, *Molecular Photoelectron Spectroscopy*, Wiley-Interscience, London, 1970, pp. 170–2.
14. D. BETTERIDGE and A. D. BAKER, *Anal. Chem.*, 1970, **42** (i), 43A.
15. A. D. BAKER and D. W. TURNER, unpublished studies.
16. R. F. LAKE and H. THOMPSON, *Proc. Roy. Soc. Lond. Sec.* A, 1970, **315**, 323.
17. A. D. BAKER, D. P. MAY and D. W. TURNER, *J. Chem. Soc.*, 1968, 22.
18. L. ASBRINK, E. LINDHOLM and O. EDQVIST, *Chem. Phys. Letters*, 1970, **5**, 609.
19. R. HOFFMAN, *J. Chem. Phys.*, 1963, **39**, 1397.
20. J. M. SCHULMAN and J. W. MOSKOWITZ, *J. Chem. Phys.*, 1965, **43**, 3287.
21. P. A. CLARK and J. L. REGLE, *J. Chem. Phys.*, 1967, **46**, 4235.
22. M. D. NEWTON, F. P. BOER and W. N. LIPSCOMB, *J. Amer. Chem. Soc.*, 1966, **88**, 2353.
23. Ref. 13, chap. 10.
24. A. D. BAKER, D. BETTERIDGE, N. R. KEMP and R. E. KIRBY, *J. Chem. Soc.* D, 1970, 286.
25. M. J. S. DEWAR, *The Electronic Theory of Organic Chemistry*, O.U.P., Oxford, 1949.
26. C. R. BRUNDLE and M. B. ROBIN, *J. Amer. Chem. Soc.*, 1970, **92**, 5550.

27. C. R. BRUNDLE, M. B. ROBIN, N. A. KEUBLER and H. BASCH, *J. Amer. Chem. Soc.*, 1972, **94**, 1451.
28. C. R. BRUNDLE and M. B. ROBIN in *Determination of Organic Structures by Physical Methods*, Vol. III (Eds. F. NACHOD and G. ZUCKERMAN, Academic Press, New York, 197.
29. W. C. PRICE, *Endeavour*, 1967, **26**, 75.
30. W. C. PRICE, *Molecular Spectroscopy*, Inst. Petroleum, 1968.
31. A. D. BAKER, *Accts. Chem. Res.*, 1970, **3**, 17.
32. C. R. BRUNDLE, *Appl. Spectroscopy*, 1971, **25**, 8.
33. D. W. TURNER in *Physical Methods in Advanced Inorganic Chemistry* (Eds. H. A. O. HILL and P. DAY), Interscience, London, 1969.
34. D. W. TURNER, *Chem. Britain*, 1968, **4**, 435.
35. D. W. TURNER, *Adv. Mass Spectrometry*, 1968, **4**, 755.
36. R. S. BERRY, *Ann. Rev. Phys. Chem.*, 1969, **20**, 357.
37. D. W. TURNER, *Proc. Roy. Soc.* A, 1968, **307**, 15.
38. C. R. BRUNDLE and D. W. TURNER, *Proc. Roy. Soc.* A, 1968, **307**, 27.
39. D. W. TURNER and D. P. MAY, *J. Chem. Phys.*, 1966, **45**, 471.
40. D. W. TURNER and D. P. MAY, *J. Chem. Phys.* 1967, **46**, 1156.
41. C. R. BRUNDLE and D. W. TURNER, *Int. J. Mass Spec. Ion Phys.*, 1969, **2**, 195.
42. J. E. COLLIN and P. NATALIS, *Int. J. Mass Spec. Ion Phys.*, 1968, **1**, 488.
43. J. E. COLLIN and P. NATALIS, *Int. J. Mass Spec. Ion Phys.*, 1968, **1**, 121.
44. J. H. D. ELAND and C. J. DANBY, *Int. J. Mass Spec. Ion Phys.*, 1968, **1**, 111.
45. J. A. R. SAMSON, *Phys. Lett.*, 1968, **28A**, 391.
46. C. R. BRUNDLE, *Chem. Phys. Lett.*, 1970, **5**, 410.
47. O. EDQVIST, E. LINDHOLM, L. E. SELIN and L. ASBRINK, *Phys. Lett.*, 1970, **31A**, 292.
48. C. R. BRUNDLE, D. NEUMANN, W. C. PRICE, D. EVANS, A. W. POTT and D. C. STREET, *J. Chem. Phys.*, 1970, **53**, 705.
49. D. C. FROST, C. A. McDOWELL and D. A. VROOM, *J. Chem. Phys.*, 1967, **46**, 4255.
50. H. J. LEMPKA, R. T. PASSMORE and W. C. PRICE, *Proc. Roy. Soc.* A, 1968, **304**, 53.
51. H. J. LEMPKA and W. C. PRICE, *J. Chem. Phys.*, 1968, **48**, 1875.
52. W. C. PRICE, *Bull. Soc. Chim. Belg.*, 1964, **73**, 318.
53. A. W. POTTS, H. J. LEMPKA, D. G. STREETS and W. C. PRICE, *Phil. Trans. Roy. Soc. Lond.* A, 1970, **268**, 59.
54. P. J. BASSETT and D. R. LLOYD, *J. Chem. Soc.* A, 1971, 1551.
55. P. J. BASSETT and D. R. LLOYD, *J. Chem. Soc.* B, 1970, 36.
56. R. J. BOYD and D. C. FROST, *Chem. Phys. Lett.*, 1968, **1**, 649.
57. C. R. BRUNDLE, M. B. ROBIN, H. BASCH, M. PINSKY and A. BOND, *J. Amer. Chem. Soc.*, 1970, **92**, 3863.
58. D. C. FROST, F. G. HERRING and C. A. McDOWELL, *Chem. Phys. Lett.*, 1970, **5**, 291.
59. D. R. LLOYD and N. LYNAUGH, *Phil. Trans. Roy. Soc. Lond.* A, 1970, **268**, 97.
60. H. B. GRAY, *Electrons and Chemical Bonding*, Benjamin, New York, 1965.
61. T. ROSE, R. FREY and B. BREHM, *J. Chem. Soc.* D, 1969, 1518.
62. T. ROSE, R. FREY and B. BREHM, *J. Chem. Soc.* D, 1970, 460.

63. F. J. BASSETT and D. R. LLOYD, *Chem. Phys. Lett.*, 1969, **3**, 22.
64. F. J. BASSETT and D. R. LLOYD, *Chem. Phys. Lett.*, 1970, **6**, 166.
65. D. C. FROST, F. G. HERRING, C. A. McDOWELL, M. R. MUSTAFA and J. S. SANDHU, *Chem. Phys. Lett.*, 1968, **2**, 663.
66. R. MANNE, *Chem. Phys. Lett.*, 1970, **5**, 125.
67. D. R. LLOYD, private communication.
68. J. DELWICHE in *Dynamic Mass Spectrometry*, Vol. 1 (Eds. J. E. WILLIAMS and D. PRICE), Heyden, London, 1970, p. 71.
69. J. DELWICHE, *Bull. Classe Sci. Acad. Roy. Belges*, 1969, **55**, 215.
70. C. R. BRUNDLE, M. B. ROBIN and G. R. JONES, *J. Chem. Phys.*, 1970, **52**, 3383.
71. E. HEILBRONNER, V. HORNUNG and K. A. MUSZKAT, *Helv. Chim. Acta*, 1970, **53**, 347.
72. S. CRADOCK and E. A. V. EBSWORTH, *J. Chem. Soc.* D, 1971, 57.
73. G. R. BRANTON, D. C. FROST, F. F. HERRING, C. A. McDOWELL and I. A. STENHOUSE, *Chem. Phys. Lett.*, 1969, **3**, 581.
74. D. W. TURNER, *Phil. Trans. Roy. Soc. Lond.* A, 1970, **268**, 7.
75. G. R. BRANTON, D. C. FROST, C. A. McDOWELL and I. A. STENHOUSE, *Chem. Phys. Lett.*, 1970, **5**, 1.
76. W. C. PRICE, private communication.
77. P. J. BASSETT, D. R. LLOYD, I. H. HILLIER and V. R. SAUNDERS, *Chem. Phys. Lett.*, 1970, **6**, 253.
78. I. H. HILLIER and V. R. SAUNDERS, *J. Chem. Soc.* D, 1970, 1510.
79. I. H. HILLIER and V. R. SAUNDERS, *J. Chem. Soc.* D, 1970, 316.
80. J. H. D. ELAND, *Phil. Trans. Roy. Soc. Lond.* A, 1970, **268**, 87.
81. D. C. FROST, C. A. McDOWELL and D. A. VROOM, *Chem. Phys. Lett.*, 1967, **1**, 93.
82. P. MITCHELL and M. WILSON, *Chem. Phys. Lett.*, 1969, **3**, 389.
83. J. H. D. ELAND, *Int. J. Mass Spec. Ion Phys.*, 1970, **4**, 37.
84. G. DISTEFANO and V. H. DIEBELER, *Int. J. Mass Spec. Ion Phys.*, 1970, **4**, 59.
85. D. R. LLOYD and E. W. SCHLOG, *Inorg. Chem.*, 1969, **8**, 2544.
86. S. EVANS, J. O. GREEN, M. L. H. GREEN, A. F. ORCHARD and D. W. TURNER, *Faraday Soc. Disc.*, 1969, 112.
87. S. EVANS, J. C. GREEN, A. F. ORCHARD, T. SAITO and D. W. TURNER, *Chem. Phys. Lett.*, 1969, **4**, 361.
88. J. C. GREEN, D. L. KING and J. H. D. ELAND, *J. Chem. Soc.* D, 1970, 1121.
89. P. J. BASSETT, Ph.D. Thesis, University of Birmingham, 1970.
90. W. T. BORDASS and J. W. LINNETT, *Nature*, 1969, **222**, 660.
91. J. BERKOWITZ and W. A. CHUPKA, *J. Chem. Phys.*, 1966, **45**, 1187.
92. N. J. RIDYARD, private communication.
93. J. BERKOWITZ, private communication.
94. A. D. BAKER, C. BAKER, C. R. BRUNDLE and D. W. TURNER, *Int. J. Mass Spec. Ion Phys.*, 1968, **1**, 285.
95. R. F. LAKE and H. THOMPSON, *Proc. Roy. Soc.* A, 1970, **317**, 187.
96. N. JONATHAN, K. ROSS and V. TOMLINSON, *Int. J. Mass Spec. Phys.*, 1970, **4**, 51.
97. E. HEILBRONNER, V. HORNUNG and ELSE KLOSTER-JENSEN, *Helv. Chim. Acta*, 1970, **53**, 331.

98. J. E. COLLIN and J. DELWICHE, *Canad. J. Chem.*, 1967, **45**, 1883.
99. C. BAKER and D. W. TURNER, *Proc. Roy. Soc.* A, 1968, **308**, 19.
100. D. C. FROST, F. G. HERRING, C. A. McDOWELL and I. A. STENHOUSE, *Chem. Phys. Lett.*, 1970, **4**, 5333.
101. H. BASCH, M. B. ROBIN, N. A. KUEBLER, C. BAKER and D. W. TURNER, *J. Chem. Phys.*, 1969, **51**, 52.
102. M. J. S. DEWAR and S. D. WORLEY, *J. Chem. Phys.*, 1969, **50**, 654.
103. N. BODOR, M. J. S. DEWAR and S. D. WORLEY, *J. Amer. Chem. Soc.*, 1970, **92**, 19.
104. M. J. S. DEWAR, B. HAZELBACH and S. D. WORLEY, *Proc. Roy. Soc.* A, 1970, **315**, 431.
105. S. D. WORLEY, *J. Chem. Soc.* D, 1970, 980.
106. M. J. S. DEWAR and S. D. WORLEY, *J. Chem. Phys.*, 1968, **49**, 2454.
107. J. L. REGLE, I. A. STENHOUSE, D. C. FROST and C. A. McDOWELL, *J. Chem. Phys.* 1970, **53**, 178.
108. J. A. HASHMALL and E. HEILBRONNER, *Angew. Chem. Int. Ed.* 1970, **9**, 305.
109. D. F. BRAILSFORD and B. FORD, *Mol. Phys.*, 1970, **18**, 621.
110. A. D. BAKER, D. BETTERIDGE, N. R. KEMP and R. E. KIRBY, *J. Mol. Struct.*, 1971, **8**, 75.
111. C. R. BRUNDLE, M. B. ROBIN, H. BASCH, M. PINSKY and A. BOND. *J. Amer. Chem. Soc.*, 1970, **93**, 3863.
112. A. K. HOLLIDAY, W. READE, R. A. W. JOHNSTONE and A. F. NEVILLE, *J. Chem. Soc.* D, 1971, **51**.
113. J. H. D. ELAND and C. J. DANBY, *Z. Naturforsch.*, 1968, **23a**, 355.
114. J. H. D. ELAND, *Int. J. Mass Spec. Ion Phys.*, 1969, **2**, 471.
115. A. D. BAKER, D. BETTERIDGE, N. R. KEMP and R. E. KIRBY, *Anal. Chem.*, 1969, **42**, 1064.
116. A. D. BAKER and D. W. TURNER, *Phil. Trans. Roy. Soc. Lond.* A, 1970, **268**, 131.
117. E. HEILBRONNER, V. HORNUNG, H. BOCK and H. ALT, *Angew Chem. Int. Ed.*, 1969, **8**, 524.
118. C. GOFFART, J. MOMIGNY and P. NATALIS, *Int. J. Mass Spec. Ion Phys.*, 1969, **3**, 371.
119. B.-O. JONNSON, E. LINDHOLM and A. SKERBELE, *ibid.*, 1969, **3**, 385.
120. M. J. S. DEWAR and S. D. WORLEY, *J. Chem. Phys.*, 1969, **51**, 263.
121. M. J. S. DEWAR and J. KELEMAN, *Tetrahedron Letters*, 1967, 2341.
122. P. BISCHOF, J. A. HASHMALL, E. HEILBRONNER and V. HORNUNG, *Helv. Chim. Acta*, 1969, **52**, 1745.
123. R. HOFFMAN, E. HEILBRONNER and R. GLEITER, *J. Amer. Chem. Soc.*, 1970, **92**, 706.
124. P. BISCHOF, J. A. HASHMALL, E. HEILBRONNER and V. HORNUNG, *Tetrahedron Letters*, 1970, 1033.
125. E. HASELBACH, J. A. HASHMALL, E. HEILBRONNER and V. HORNUNG, *Angew Chem. Int. Ed.*, 1969, **8**, 878.
126. E. HASELBACH and E. HEILBRONNER, *Helv. Chim. Acta*, 1970, **53**, 684.
127. E. HEILBRONNER and K. A. MUSZKAT, *J. Amer. Chem. Soc.*, 1970, **92**, 3818.
128. A. D. BAKER, C. R. BRUNDLE and D. W. TURNER, *Int. J. Mass Spec. Ion Phys.*, 1968, **1**, 443.

129. J. MOMIGNY, C. GOFFART and L. D'OR, *Int. J. Mass Spec. Ion Phys.*, 1968, **1**, 53.
130. P. NATALIS, J. DELWICHE and J. E. COLLINS, *Chem. Phys. Lett.*, 1971, **9**, 139.
131. D. W. TURNER, *Ann. Rev. Phys. Chem.*, 1970, 107.
132. W. B. DORMSTADT, *Messtechnik*, 1970, **78**, 133.
133. L. ASBRINK, *Chem. Phys. Lett.*, 1970, **7**, 549.
134. H. HOTOP and A. NIEHAUS, *Int. J. Mass Spec. Ion. Phys.*, 1970, **5**, 415.
135. T. A. CARLSON, *Chem. Phys. Lett.*, 1971, **9**, 23.
136. N. JONATHAN, A. MORRIS, D. J. SMITH and K. J. RON, *Chem. Phys. Lett.*, 1970, **7**, 497.
137. C. R. BRUNDLE, *Chem. Phys. Lett.*, 1970, **7**, 317.
138. O. EDQVIST, E. LINDHOLM, L. E. SELIN, H. SJOGREN and L. ASBRINK, *Arkin Fysik*, 1970, **40**, 439.
139. J. DELWICHE, P. NATALIS and J. E. COLLINS, *Int. J. Mass Spec. Ion Phys.*, 1970, **5**, 443.
140. P. A. COX, S. EVANS, A. HAMMETT and A. F. ORCHARD, *Chem. Phys. Lett.*, 1970, **7**, 414.
141. P. J. BASSETT and D. R. LLOYD, *J. Chem. Soc.* A, 1971, 641.
142. W. E. BULL, B. P. PULLEN, F. A. GRIMM, W. E. MODDEMAN, G. K. SCHWEITZER and T. A. CARLSON, *Inorg. Chem.*, 1970, **9**, 2474.
143. J. C. GREEN, M. L. H. GREEN, P. J. JOACHIM, A. F. ORCHARD, and D. W. TURNER, *Phil. Trans. Roy. Soc. Lond.* A, 1970, **268**, 111.
144. H. BOCH and W. FUSS, *Angew Chem.* (*Int. Ed.*), 1971, **10**, 182.
145. D. R. LLOYD and N. LYNAUGH, *J. Chem. Soc.* D, 1971, 125.
146. A. K. HOLLIDAY, W. READE, R. A. W. JOHNSTONE and A. F. NEVILLE, *J. Chem. Soc.* D, 1971, 51.
147. D. R. LLOYD and N. LYNAUGH, *J. Chem. Soc.* D, 1970, 1545.
148. D. R. LLOYD, *Int. J. Mass Spec. Ion Phys.*, 1970, **4**, 500.
149. B. J. COCKSEY, J. H. D. ELAND and C. J. DANBY, *J. Chem. Soc.* B, 1971, 790.
150. N. BODOR, M. J. S. DEWAR, W. B. JENNINGS and S. D. WORLEY, *Tetrahedron*, 1970, **26**, 4109.
151. D. A. DEMES and A. J. YENCHA, *J. Chem. Phys.*, 1970, **53**, 4536.
152. E. HASELBACH, *Chem. Phys. Lett.*, 1970, **7**, 428.
153. P. BISCHOF, E. HASELBACH and E. HEILBRONNER, *Angew Chem.* (*Int. Ed.*), 1970, **9**, 953.
154. P. BISCHOF and E. HEILBRONNER, *Helv. Chim. Acta*, 1970, **53**, 1677.
155. P. BISCHOF, R. GLEITER, E. HEILBRONNER, V. HORNUNG and G. SCHRODER, *Helv. Chim. Acta*, 1970, **53**, 1645.
156. R. GLEITER, E. HEILBRONNER and A. DE MEIJEVE, *Helv. Chim. Acta*, 1971, **54**, 1029.
157. P. BISCHOF, E. HEILBRONNER, H. PRINZBACH and H. D. MARTIN, *Helv. Chim. Acta*, 1971, **54**, 1072.
158. E. HASELBACH, E. HEILBRONNER, A. MANNSCHRECK and W. SEITZ, *Angew Chem.* (*Int. Ed.*), 1970, **9**, 902.
159. R. GLEITER, E. HEILBRONNER and V. HORNUNG, *Angew Chem.* (*Int. Ed.*), 1970, **9**, 901.
160. S. PIGNATARO, V. MANCINI, J. N. A. RIDYARD and H. J. LEMPKA, *J. Chem. Soc.* D, 1971, 142.

161. P. Bischof, R. Gleiter and E. Heilbronner, *Helv. Chim. Acta*, 1970, **53,** 1425.
162. R. Hoffman, *Acct. Chem. Res.*, 1971, **4,** 1.
163. P. A. Cox and F. A. Orchard, *Chem. Phys. Lett.*, 1970, **7,** 273.
164. L. C. Lohr Jr., and M. B. Robin, *J. Amer. Chem. Soc.*, 1970, **92,** 7241.

CHAPTER 5

STRUCTURAL EFFECTS ON CORE ELECTRON BINDING ENERGIES AND X-RAY PHOTO-ELECTRON SPECTRA

CHEMICAL SHIFTS

(A) GENERAL COMMENTS

In the previous chapter we dealt chiefly with effects of structure and substitution upon valence-shell (VUV) photoelectron spectra. Since valence-shell electrons are directly involved in bonding, they are very sensitive to substituent and other structural effects, but because the molecular orbitals they occupy are generally multi-centred, it is not usually possible to identify the individual elements of a molecule from its valence-shell PE spectrum. This difficulty is compounded by the fact that many different types of valence-shell orbital have very similar energies, with resultant overlap of adjacent bands in photoelectron spectra.

Core electrons within a molecule do retain their atomic identity to a great extent, however, and therefore X-ray photoelectron spectroscopy is able to provide an elemental analysis, the presence of a particular element being inferred from the spectrum by the presence of a peak characteristic of the element's K-shell (or other inner shell) electrons. Thus fluorine always gives rise to a peak near 690 eV. Core electrons do nevertheless suffer *small* changes in binding energy as their environment is changed. These changes or "chemical shifts" are due to the electrostatic interaction between

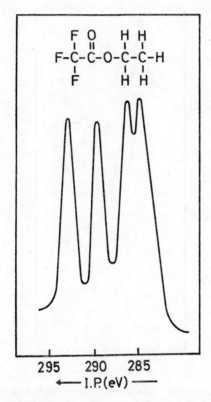

FIG. 5.1. C 1s part of the X-ray photoelectron spectrum of ethyltrifluoro acetate.[1]

the valence and the core electrons, and allow structural deductions to be made from X-ray photoelectron spectra.

The relative changes ($< 5\%$) in the binding energies of core electrons in different environments are small in comparison with relative changes in valence shell binding energies (up to 20%). Nevertheless, on an absolute scale, the changes (up to 12 eV) are often comparable to, or even greater than, absolute changes in the energies of the valence electrons, and thus may be detected by X-ray PES.

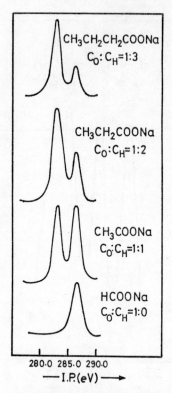

FIG. 5.2. C 1s part of the X-ray photoelectron spectrum of the sodium salts of some aliphatic carboxylic acids.[1]

Atoms in different environments and different oxidation states may, for example, be identified by the presence of different peaks within the X-ray PE spectrum. Some simple examples follow which illustrate this sort of effect.

The chemical structure dependence of carbon core–electron binding energies is clearly of particular relevance to the organic chemist. In this connection, the carbon 1s part of the X-ray PE spectrum of ethyl trifluoroacetate (Fig. 5.1) is often used to demonstrate the potential of the technique.[1] The four peaks in the C 1s region, in a near perfect $1:1:1:1$ intensity ratio, demonstrate nicely the presence of carbon atoms in four different environments.

Several other examples of C 1s chemical shifts and the use of photoelectron peak intensities appear in the literature. Thus, the carbon 1s binding energy in gaseous methane is $-290\cdot8$ eV, whereas in gaseous carbon tetrafluoride it is $-301\cdot8$ eV.[2] In the C 1s region of the PE spectrum of $(CH_3)_4C$, two peaks whose intensities are in the ratio $4:1$ can be seen, indicating the presence of carbon atoms in two different environments in the correct relative abundances. A final simple example of the use of C 1s chemical shifts is afforded by the photoelectron spectra of the series of compounds HCOONa, CH_3COONa, C_2H_5COONa, and n-C_3H_7COONa.[1] Within the C 1s part of the photoelectron spectra of these sodium salts, one peak corresponding to the carbon atom attached to oxygen, and another peak corresponding to the carbon atoms of the alkyl chain can be discerned (see Fig. 5.2). The relative heights of the two peaks gives the number of carbon atoms in the chain in every case. As might be expected, however, for compounds containing many carbon atoms the different C 1s peaks overlap to such an extent that simple deductions from the spectra may be difficult. Improved resolution and improved deconvolution techniques could conceivably improve this situation, although the natural width of the X-ray exciting line imposes a fundamental limit.

Many examples of chemical shifts for atoms other than carbon have been reported in the literature for both organic and inorganic compounds (a selection is included in the tables and charts at the end of the book). Among the more spectacular successes of X-ray PES are the demonstration of the presence of three N 1s peaks in the ratio of $4:2:1$ for the compound trans-dinitrobis (ethylenediamine) cobalt(III) nitrate, $[Co(NH_2CH_2CH_2NH_2)_2(NO_2)_2]NO_3$,[3] the detection of the single cobalt atom in the PE spectrum of vitamin B_{12},[1] and the detection of the two different types of sulphur atoms in the PE spectrum of phthalylsulphathiazole.[4]

Phthalylsulphathiazole

More recently, Clark and Barber[5] have also reported both N 1s and C 1s binding energies distinguishing the different nitrogen and carbon atoms within the three nucleic acid adenine, cytosine and thymine. These results are presented schematically in Fig. 5.3. Clark and Barber did not show the actual spectra in their paper reporting these results, so it is impossible to say how well resolved were the individual peaks. It seems likely, however, that it would have been quite difficult to resolve separate carbon and separate

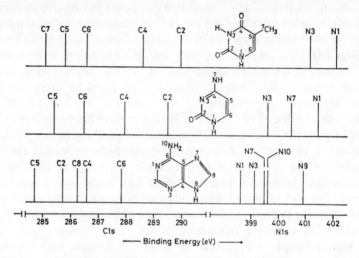

FIG. 5.3. Schematic representation of the different C 1s and N 1s binding energies for the nucleic acid bases, adenine, thymine and cytosine.

nitrogen peaks for all the different C and N atoms in the spectra of such complex compounds without using spectrum deconvolution techniques.

Electron binding energies and electronic configurations lie, of course, at the very heart of chemistry as a subject and are accordingly interesting to study *per se* for fundamental reasons. However, PES has already been used in a more practical sense, both to deduce unknown structures, and more generally in other areas of analysis. The use of X-ray PES in structure determinations is illustrated by the nitrogen 1s spectrum of $Na_2N_2O_3$ (see Fig. 5.4), as reported by

Hendrickson and co-workers.[6] Three possible structures for the oxyhyponitrite ion had been postulated before the X-ray PES work:

$$O{=}N - O - N^{-}{-} O^{-} \qquad O{=}N - N\overset{\displaystyle O^{-}}{\underset{\displaystyle O^{-}}{<}} \qquad {}^{-}O - N{=}N - O - O^{-}$$

(I) (II) (III)

The photoelectron spectrum of $Na_2N_2O_3$ clearly shows the presence of structurally non-equivalent nitrogen atoms, and this rules out the symmetrical structure (I). MO calculations and detailed considerations of the actual binding energy values observed further showee that only structure (II) was compatible with all the observations.

A second structural problem to which X-ray PES has been successfully applied concerns disulphide dioxides.[1] Two possible structures (IV) and (V)

$$\begin{array}{cc} R - S - S - R & \overset{\displaystyle O}{\underset{}{R - S - \overset{\uparrow}{S} - R}} \\ \downarrow \quad \downarrow & \downarrow \\ O \quad\; O & O \\ \text{(IV)} & \text{(V)} \end{array}$$

had been suggested. The photoelectron spectrum of cysteine disulphur dioxide, however, revealed two sulphur core lines, which conclusively establishes that structure (V) is the correct one.

It has already been pointed out that X-ray PES cannot always distinguish atoms in different environments, especially if they are very similar. For example, the different carbon atoms of the ethyl and propyl chains of sodium acetate and sodium propionate are not distinguished by their C 1s photoelectron spectra (Fig. 5.2). Even atoms in quite different environments or oxidation states do not always appear to show up in PE spectra as separate peaks with the appropriate relative intensities. Thus, Brundle and Robin[7] have already pointed out that the X-ray PE spectrum of Prussian

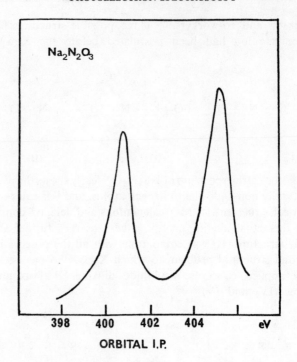

$Na_2N_2O_3$

398   400   402   404   eV

ORBITAL I.P.

FIG. 5.4. N 1s part of the X-ray photoelectron spectrum of $Na_2N_2O_3$.[6]

Blue, KFe_4 [$Fe(CN_6)$]) does not contain two peaks in the 1:1 ratio expected from the Fe^{2+} and Fe^{3+} states of iron which are suggested to exist in Prussian Blue on the grounds of Mossbauer spectroscopy. In this connection the X-ray PE spectra of the normal and invert spinels, e.g. Mn_3O_4, Fe_3O_4, should provide informative test cases since their oxidation states have been fully investigated as a result of the development of ligand field theory.

In spite of possible shortcomings in certain cases, however, X-ray PES is clearly going to become an important complementary spectroscopic technique for the determination of molecular structure, as is exemplified by a recent study which has established how sulphur and oxygen atoms are linked to carbon in the products resulting

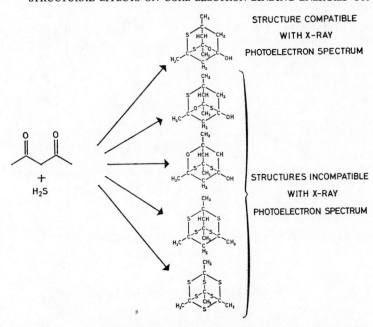

Fig. 5.5. Illustration of how ESCA can help determine which of several possible products is formed in a reaction.

from the reactions between H_2S and (i) 2,4 pentanedione and (ii) α-angelicalactone.[8] The PES work resolved which of several possible structural formulae for the reaction products were correct (see Figs. 5.5 and 5.6).

(B) CORRELATIONS OF CHEMICAL SHIFTS WITH OTHER PARAMETERS

The application of ESCA to the solution of structural problems can clearly be simplified by developing methods for predicting reasonably accurately the binding energy values for any structural formulae one might propose for a given compound. The agreement or otherwise between the experimentally measured binding energies for the compound in question and the predicted values for the proposed

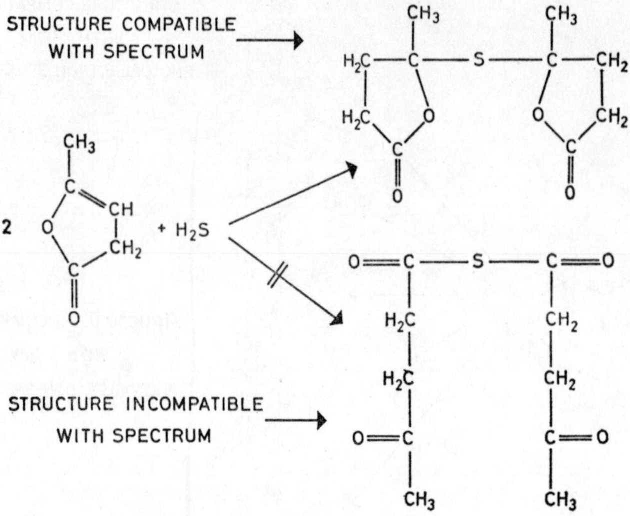

FIG. 5.6. Structures differentiated by ESCA.

structure would then prove the latter correct or incorrect. It is not surprising, therefore, that the connection between the chemical shifts observed in ESCA and the natures of the changes taking place in the environment of the atom concerned have aroused considerable interest.

A simple model for approximating core electron-binding energy changes can be demonstrated by reference to an atom A reacting with a second atom B to form a 100% ionic compound $A^{n+}B^{n-}$. The *total* removal of n-electrons from the valence shell of A would be expected to lower the energy of an inner shell electron by an amount, ΔE, which is proportional to n and inversely proportional to the radius of the valence shell orbit, as expressed in equation (5.1) where k is a constant.

$$\Delta E = k\, \frac{n}{r} \qquad (5.1)$$

Thus ΔE should change with n—for instance, ΔE for Fe^{2+} should differ from ΔE for Fe^{3+}. In the formation of $A^{n+}B^{n-}$, however, the

n-electrons removed from A do not go to infinity, but into the valence shell of B, so that if the internuclear separation of A and B is R, equation (5.1) must be modified to

$$\Delta E = k \left[\frac{1}{r} - \frac{1}{R} \right].$$ (5.2)

In a crystalline lattice, we would also have to make allowance for the Madelung constant, α, and this could be done by replacing the $1/R$ term of equation (5.2) by α/R.

The above model, which implies that all compounds are 100% ionic, is of course inapplicable to most real systems, and other methods have to be sought to predict binding energies. Some are based on correlations with "charge densities", others are based on non-empirical MO calculations, and yet others depend on the use of thermochemical data. These methods will now be considered briefly.

(i) *Partial charges*

The simple ionic approach can be extended by considering the effective or partial charges on atoms within a molecule. It has been argued initially by Pauling [9] and more extensively by Sanderson[10] that the partial charge on each atom within a molecule can be calculated by consideration of the electronegativities and arrangement of the constituent atoms. Sanderson further argued that a group electronegativity can be calculated for common chemical groupings. Since the arguments are based on electronegativities, some "covalent corrections" are automatically made, and he has correctly predicted the properties of many compounds by using this approach.

Siegbahn and his associates have developed these sort of arguments by correlating chemical shifts and partial charges.[1] They consider the charge, q, on an atom within a particular compound to be given by equation (5.3) where Q is the formal charge and I_N is the partial ionic character summed over all the bonds involving the atom

$$q = Q + \sum_N I_N$$ (5.3)

I_N is estimated from the difference in electronegativities between the atoms forming a bond. This can be done by using Pauling's relation relating electronegativity difference with partial ionic character of a bond:[9]

$$I = 1 - \exp\left[-0.25(\chi_A - \chi_B)^2\right] \qquad (5.4)$$

Where χ_A and χ_B are the electronegativities of the two atoms involved in forming the bond. A more detailed account of the method of calculation is given in Appendix 5.

Linear graphs are often obtained when measured core electron binding energies are plotted against the charges on the atom concerned calculated in the above way. For example, a good linear plot results from a graph of the measured C 1s binding energies of bromomethanes (CH_4, CH_3Br, CH_2Br_2, $CHBr_3$ and CBr_4) against the atomic charges on carbon calculated from Pauling electronegativities,[11] i.e. for carbon 2·5, for bromine 2·8 and for hydrogen 2·1.

A similar straight-line plot is obtained for fluoromethanes (fluorine electronegativity = 4·0), but interestingly, the points from the bromomethane and fluoromethanes do not lie on the same straight line.

This discrepancy is probably due to the fairly high percentage (*ca.* 20%) of s-character of the bromine valence orbital in the bromomethane compounds, because when 3·3 is used as the electronegativity of bromine instead of 2·8 (corresponding to 20% s-character), both the fluoromethane and bromomethane points do line on one straight line. This example highlights the necessity for care in comparing different families of compounds.

Although fairly good straight line plots like the above are quite frequently obtained for families of carbon compounds, extremely poor correlations have been reported in other cases, e.g. for oxygen compounds (Fig. 5.7). As Siegbahn and his colleagues point out, however, it is rather surprising in view of the primitive way of calculating the atomic charge that such good correlations as the ones for carbon compounds are obtained.

Molecular orbital calculations provide a more rigorous technique for calculating charge densities. Both semi-empirical methods, such as the extended Huckel method and the CNDO ("complete neglect of differential overlap") method,[11] and non-empirical all-electron *ab initio* methods have been tried.

Siegbahn *et al.* have compared the types of correlation graphs

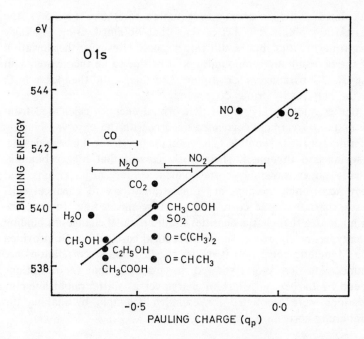

FIG. 5.7. Plot of partial charge on oxygen atoms (found from Pauling Electro-negativities) against O 1s binding energies.[11]

obtained by using Pauling electronegativity calculated charges and CNDO calculated charges (cf. Figs. 5.7 and 5.8). The calculated chemical shift, ΔE, for the CNDO graph comes from the equation:

$$\Delta E = kq_A + V + l \qquad (5.5)$$

where q_A is the charge difference on an atom A between the molecule under consideration and a reference molecule, and V is the inter-atomic effective potential, or molecular potential found from:

$$V = \sum_{B \neq A} \frac{q_A}{R_{AB}} \qquad (5.6)$$

The parameters k and l of equation (5.5) are determined by a least squares plot to fit the experimental data.

When the energy shift for O 1s relative to O_2 is compared with calculated shifts according to equation (5.5) (see Fig. 5.7), the correlation obtained is better than that obtained using Pauling's electronegativities, but is still rather poor. However, the deviation of the two sulphur compounds could be due to an inconsistency in the CNDO parameters for sulphur, and this would then leave N_2O as the only really serious discrepancy.[11]

Barber and Clark[5] found that orbital energies calculated from an *ab initio* treatment correlated linearly with the observed binding energies for the C 1s and N 1s levels in the nucleic acid bases adenine, cytosine and thymine.† Their work showed that higher binding-energy values sometimes corresponded to more negative ions, and they accordingly pointed out that straightforward chemical shift versus partial charge correlations can be misleading. In fact, the original idea that charge densities should parallel changes in binding energy has no rigorously sound theoretical basis, although, provided the Madelung correction is made, excellent linear correlations are found. Van der Avoird showed, for example, that the deviations found by Barber and Clark in charge versus shift straight line correlations were accounted for completely simply by making the Madelung correction.[12]

(ii) *The principle of equivalent cores*

Jolly and his associates have developed an ingenious method for predicting core electron binding energies by employing only thermochemical data.[13] Their method is based on the principle of equivalent cores, which relies on the approximation that when a core electron is removed from an atom in a molecule or ion, the valence electrons relax as if the nuclear charge had increased by one unit. Thus atomic cores (i.e. nuclei plus core shells) having the same net charge can be considered to be chemically equivalent. The usefulness of this concept can be illustrated with reference to some nitrogen containing compounds. The binding energies of the N 1s electrons in N_2 and NH_3 are given by respectively equations (5.7) and (5.8) where the asterisks indicate vacancies in the cores of the N atoms.

†Deviations of up to 2 eV are, however, to be expected owing to the similar variations in relaxion energies in different compounds of the same element, e.g. after C 1s ionizations the relaxion energies in CH_4 and CO are respectively 14·40 and 12·31 eV.

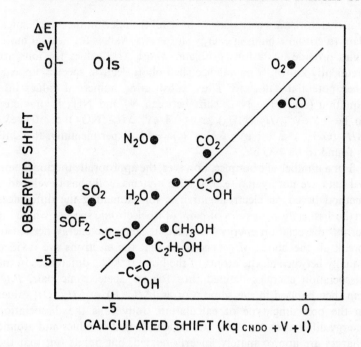

FIG. 5.8. Plot of experimentally observed O 1s binding energy shifts (relative to O_2) against shifts calculated by using the theoretical CNDO molecular orbital approach.[11]

$$[N \ 1s \ B.E.(N_2)] = \Delta H_f \, (NN^*)^+ - \Delta H_f \, (N_2), \qquad (5.7)$$

$$[N \ 1s \ B.E.(NH_3)] = \Delta H_f \, (N^*H_3)^+ - \Delta H_f \, (NH_3). \qquad (5.8)$$

Since N^* has the same core charge as O, we can replace the above two equations by equations (5.9) and (5.10) according to the above principle.

$$[N \ 1s \ B.E.(N_2)] = \Delta H_f \, (NO)^+ - \Delta H_f \, (N_2), \qquad (5.9)$$

$$[N \ 1s \ B.E.(NH_3)] = \Delta H_f \, (OH_3)^+ - \Delta H_f \, (NH_3). \qquad (5.10)$$

Thus the shift in N 1s binding energies for N_2 and NH_3 can be found from equation (5.11).

$$[N \ 1s \ B.E.(NH_3)] - [N \ 1s \ B.E.(N_2)] =$$
$$\Delta H_f \, (OH_3)^+ - \Delta H_f \, (NH_3) - \Delta H_f \, (NO)^+ + \Delta H_f \, (N_2). \quad (5.11)$$

It is therefore only necessary to have all the relevant thermochemical data to estimate binding energy shifts. ΔH_f values for neutral molecules provide no serious problem, whilst ΔH_f values for ions are frequently known from valence shell photoelectron spectra, appearance potential data, etc. Thus, substituting numerical values into equation (5.11), the N 1s shift between N_2 and NH_3 is predicted to be 3·5 eV [ΔH_f (NH_3) $\simeq$ −0·4 eV, ΔH_f (NO^+) $\simeq$ 10·0 eV; ΔH_f (OH_3^+) $\simeq$ 6·1 eV; ΔH_f (N_2) $= 0$]. Experimentally, the shift is found to be 4·35 eV.

For a number of examples, however, the appropriate thermochemical data are not available. For such systems, Jolly has developed a method based on electronegativities for estimating the differences in the dissociation energies of pairs of isoelectronic species, where the term " dissociation energy" is taken as being the energy needed to break all the bonds of a species so that the electrons are divided equally between all the atoms of the bond.[14] The differences in the dissociation energies defined thus for an isoelectronic pair, P,Q, can then be used in the same way as [ΔH_f (P) $-$ ΔH_f (Q)] values in the preceding type of calculation. Jolly calls the dissociation energy differences Δ-values, and concludes that Δ-values and atomic charges are approximately linearly related, but points out that the Δ and the other thermochemical values are more fundamentally significant for correlating core electron-binding energies. However, as Jolly also points out, there are theoretical reasons for doubting whether either isoelectronic pair energy differences or atomic charges can always correlate well with binding energies.

Finally, Jolly has put forward "partial shift" factors for different atoms. These "partial shifts" can be used to predict C 1s binding energies relative to methane. One simply adds together the partial shift (p) factors for all the atoms directly bonded to carbon in order to obtain the total shift. The values of p proposed are: H, −0·15; C, 0·55; N, 1·00; O, 2·21; F, 2·84; S, 1·04; Cl, 1·52; Br, 1·33. These values often give a reasonable estimate of the total chemical shift, although serious deviations can be encountered, as with all the other methods.

(iii) *Correlation with Mossbauer shifts*

Shifts in Mossbauer spectroscopy relate to the same sort of charge effects as do shifts in ESCA. It is interesting to note, therefore, that there is a linear correlation between Mossbauer chemical shifts and 4*d* binding energies of Sn as measured by ESCA for the series $Y_2Sn(Ox)_2$ where Ox = 8-quinolinolato and Y = Et, Ph, Cl, Br or I.[15] Similar families of straight-line graphs would therefore be expected for series of compounds in which the stereochemical and valence states of the central atom are constant.

REFERENCES

1. K. Siegbahn et al., *ESCA-Atomic, Molecular, and Solid State Structure Studied by means of Electron Spectroscopy*, Almquist & Wiksells, Uppsala, 1967.
2. J. Hedman, P. F. Heden, C. Nordling and K. Siegbahn, *Phys. Lett.* 1969, **29A**, 178.
3. D. N. Hendrickson, J. M. Hollander and W. L. Jolly, *Inorg. Chem.*, 1969, **8**, 2642.
4. C. Nordling, S. Hagstrom and K. Siegbahn, *Z. Phys.*, 1964, **138**, 443; also see *Nature*, 1966, **210**, 4.
5. M. Barber and D. T. Clark, *Chem. Comm.*, 1970, 22, and 1970, 24.
6. J. M. Hollander and W. L. Jolly, *Accts. Chem. Res.*, 1970, **3**, 1.
7. C. R. Brundle and M. B. Robin, in *Determinations of Organic Structures by Physical Methods*, Vol. III (F. Nachod and G. Zuckerman, Eds.), Academic Press, New York (to be published).
8. J. Hedman, P. F. Heden, R. Nordberg, C. Nordling and B. J. Lindberg, *Spectrochim. Acta*, 1970, **26A**, 761.
9. L. Pauling, *The Nature of the Chemical Bond*, 1st ed., Cornell U.P., 1939 (3rd ed. 1960 gives different values).
10. R. T. Sanderson, *Inorganic Chemistry*, Reinhold, New York, 1967.
11. K. Siegbahn et al., *ESCA Applied to Free Molecules*, North Holland, Amsterdam, 1970.
12. A. van der Avoird, *Chem. Comm.*, 1970, 727.
13. W. L. Jolly and D. N. Hendrickson, *J. Amer. Chem. Soc.*, 1970, **92**, 1863.
14. W. L. Jolly, *J. Amer. Chem. Soc.*, 1970, **92**, 3260.
15. M. Barber, P. Swift, D. Cunningham and M. J. Frazer, *Chem. Comm.*, 1970, 1338.

CHAPTER 6

ANALYTICAL APPLICATIONS

INTRODUCTION

It is to be expected that a technique which is applicable to all elements, serves to detect elements and provides structural information will be of considerable analytical value. As yet there have been comparatively few truly analytical studies of PES, but these have served to confirm the potential of the technique. In particular, X-ray PES has proven of value in the analysis of surfaces and in determining molecular structures, and UV-PES, in addition to providing the sort of information which is obtainable from infrared or NMR spectroscopy, has shown evidence of orbital interactions. Naturally, the compounds most studied are those best understood, but this has given rise to the false argument that the information obtained by PES, and especially, UV-PES, is equally well obtainable by infrared, NMR and mass spectrometry. Developments in technique and improvements in interpretive skill are rapidly taking place so that its versatility will become apparent. At this point it seems that by virtue of its sensitivity, ability to look at surfaces and the information it yields about compounds containing halogens, sulphur and phosphorus it should prove a valuable complementary spectroscopic technique. At present, X-ray PES appears to many to be more attractive, but because UV-PES is cheaper, has greater scope for improvement and has the backing of MO theory, both will come to be part of the analyst's armamentarium.

There are limitations as well as advantages, and this chapter is concerned with both.

ANALYSIS BY X-RAY PES (ESCA)

Hercules has reviewed the analytical potential of ESCA.[1]

(A) SAMPLE

The sample is generally in the solid form although spectra can be obtained from vapours and, in principle, liquids. Solids are prepared for analysis by pressing them into a copper mesh or dusting them onto adhesive tape. Gases and liquids may also be run as solids by condensing them, in the target chamber, onto a nitrogen-cooled metal rod in the source position. The smallest sample is largely dictated by the difficulties of handling; spectra are routinely obtained from microgram amounts of material. The X-ray penetration is not great (approx. 100 A) so it is important to ensure that the surface is representative of the bulk of the sample. The sensitivity is closely related to resolution and statistics of counting. A quick scan may take 20 minutes, but several hours may be required to obtain a fully detailed spectrum. The length of time will depend upon the resolution sought, but a rough guide is provided from the consideration that the standard deviation of a count, N, is given by the square root of the number of counts, $\sqrt{N}$, and that approximately 95% of the results will fall within two standard deviations. Therefore the minimum number of counts required to give an accuracy within 10% is 400. Count rates range from 10 to 20,000 c/min, so that 400 counts may take between 0·02–40 minutes and to cover several eV in 0·1 eV steps could take some time. With these considerations in mind, one cannot but admire the painstaking care which Siegbahn's group have taken in obtaining the spectra of hundreds of compounds and understand why it was that only rarely were full spectra reported in their early work.

(B) CALIBRATION

Having a solid sample makes calibration fairly difficult. In the first place the binding energy zero for a solid is chosen at the Fermi level whereas for a free molecule it is defined with respect to the expelled electron at rest at infinity. The energy difference between the

Fermi level and the vacuum level is the work function. Secondly, secondary electrons in the target chamber may set up a surface charge on the sample, and this will affect the energy of the ejected electron. The Fermi level and the surface charge may be affected by the nature of the sample, so that a convenient reference system is required. The one most often used is the carbon 1s line in the adhesive tape backing the sample or in the pump oil contaminating the surface of the sample. This line can then be periodically calibrated absolutely by relating it with Cu $2p_{3/2}$ and Zn $2p_{3/2}$ lines excited simultaneously with MgK_α and AlK_α radiation[2] or by comparison with graphitic carbon dusted onto the adhesive tape. The former procedure gives the carbon 1s binding energy to be 285·0 ± 0·4 eV.

Chemical shifts and fine structure of the order of 0·1 eV can be measured but in these cases it is clearly desirable to run samples for comparison as close together as possible. Also, in view of the demonstrated non-linearity over a small range for UV-PES, it is wise not to place great reliance on values referred to carbon 1s which are hundreds of eV away.

QUALITATIVE ANALYSIS

X-ray PES is arguably the most useful technique for identification that has come to hand in the last decade. It can detect the presence of all the elements present in a sample, indicate the atomic ratios, show whether the atoms of a given element are in equivalent positions or not and indicate the oxidation state of an element within the molecule. Many examples are given in the books and reviews of Siegbahn.[3-7] As was shown in Chapter 5, the binding energy of an atom within the molecule reflects its environment. Thus it should be possible to construct correlation tables which would serve to identify the oxidation state of an atom within the molecule and thereby help to identify the molecule. Two such tables are shown for sulphur containing compounds in Figs. 6.1 and 6.2. These are clearly useful guides, but a cautionary note is sounded by Jack and Hercules who examined the spectra of fifty compounds containing quaternary nitrogen.[8] They found a 5-eV spread of binding energies,

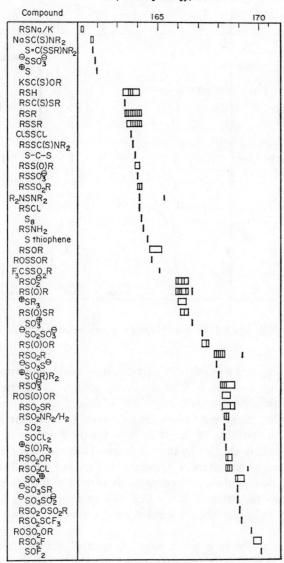

FIG. 6.1. S 2p electron binding energies for sulphur-containing compounds.
R = alkyl or aryl carbon.
Note increase in binding energy with oxidation state.

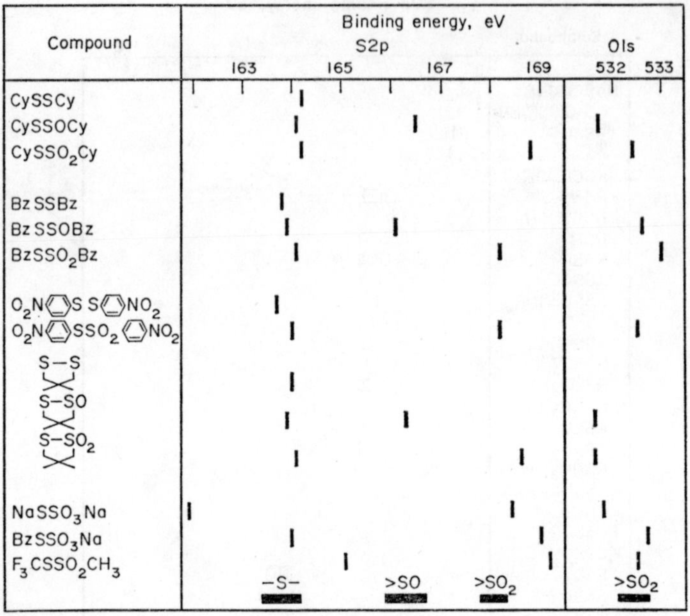

Binding energy, eV — S2p (163, 165, 167, 169) — O1s (532, 533)

Compound	S2p binding energy
$CySSCy$	
$CySSOCy$	
$CySSO_2Cy$	
$BzSSBz$	
$BzSSOBz$	
$BzSSO_2Bz$	
$O_2N\langle\rangle S\ S\langle\rangle NO_2$	
$O_2N\langle\rangle SSO_2\langle\rangle NO_2$	
$S-S$	
$S-SO$	
$S-SO_2$	
$NaSSO_3Na$	
$BzSSO_3Na$	
$F_3CSSO_2CH_3$	

$-S-$　　$>SO$　　$>SO_2$　　$>SO_2$

Fig. 6.2. S 2p and O1s electron binding energies for oxidized disulphides.

thus showing that a quaternary nitrogen atom could not be positively identified by a single peak in the X-ray spectrum. However, they did find that its presence might be inferred from the results if several other peaks were taken into account. One of their findings was that the position of the N 1s peak for the ammonium halides was appreciably affected by the halide ion. Their values for the N 1s binding energy are given in Appendix 4. This and the full study of carbon[9] and platinum[11] compounds carried out by Siegbahn's group show the value of X-ray PES as a qualitative tool. It seems especially valuable when several formal oxidation states may be expected.

Comparatively little work has been carried out with mixtures. Siegbahn et al.[5] have run simple gas mixtures. To show the scope of the method gases containing the same atom have been mixed, e.g. CO, CO_2, CH_4, N_2, NH_3. The peak separations are sufficiently good to allow both qualitative and quantitative analysis (Fig. 6.3).

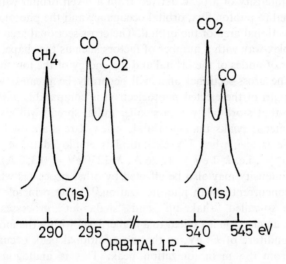

FIG. 6.3. X-ray PE spectrum of gas mixture of CO, CO_2 and CH_4 in ratio 2:1:2.

The gas-phase spectrum of a given compound may be appreciably different to the solid-phase spectrum. The peak positions are shifted, for the reasons given above, but condensed species may lack several of the distinctive features of the free molecule and this will be reflected in the spectrum. For example, the gas phase spectrum of acetic acid clearly shows two O 1s peaks corresponding to =O and —OH, but in the solid extensive hydrogen bonding renders the oxygen equivalent and the spectrum shows a single band for O 1s (Fig. 6.4). A similar effect is shown with water (Fig. 3.12).

QUANTITATIVE ANALYSIS

It is generally held that the area of peak in an X-ray PE spectrum is directly proportional to the number of atoms of the element from which it derives. Consequently it appears that the peak areas in the spectrum can provide an elemental analysis. This is true but even a casual examination of published spectra show that the application of the theory is not straightforward.

The intensity of a peak derived from a given orbital will be proportional to photon flux, orbital occupancy and the photoionization cross-sectional area of the orbital. The cross-sectional area varies in a complex way with a number of factors such as the shape, size and number of nodes of the orbital and the energy of the ionizing radiation. The cross-sectional area will generally be greatest when the wavelength of the ejected photoelectron is comparable with orbital size, so that s-orbitals with a smaller radial spread will give rise to more intense peaks than p-orbitals when X-rays are used, and the converse is true when UV excitation is employed (λ, $A = 12 \cdot 263$ (E, eV)$^{-1/2}$, i.e. λ, 1 eV = 12·26 A; λ, 1230 eV = 0·350 A).

The intensity may also be affected by other processes which take place concurrently with photoionization.[11] The principle of these are the so-called "shake-up" and "shake-out" processes. In the former, an electron is excited to a higher level within the molecule at an expenditure of E^* eV, so that an additional peak occurs E^* eV away from the main ionization peak. This is analogous to fine structure in UV-PE spectra (pp. 31–37). The "shake-out" process is that in which another electron is ejected after the photoelectron. This gives rise to double ionization and an increase in the background counts (Chapter 1). These processes always take place when X-ray PE spectra are run, and may be important—for example, the "shake-up" peak may be 10–15% of the intensity associated main peak.

The cross-section may also vary with the incident photon angle so that the peak intensity is dependent upon the geometry of the relevant parts of the spectrometer.

Notwithstanding these difficulties, Gelius has shown how it is possible to calculate the intensities of X-ray PE spectra in the 10–50 eV energy range.[12] The basis of the argument is that the ionization cross-sectional area for a molecular orbital is the sum of the cross-sectional areas of the atomic orbitals which contribute to it, and that the intensity is proportional to the product of the cross-sectional area

of the molecular orbital and its electron density. This may be
expressed by the equations

$$\sigma_j^{MO} = \sum_A \sigma_{Aj} \tag{6.1}$$

$$\sigma_{Aj} = \sum_\lambda P_{A\lambda j} \sigma_{A\lambda}^{AO} \tag{6.2}$$

$$\sigma_j^{MO} = \sum_{A,\lambda} P_{A\lambda j} \sigma_A^{AO} \tag{6.3}$$

where σ_j^{MO} and σ_{Aj} are the cross-sectional areas of the j molecular
orbital and an atomic orbital contributing to the molecular orbital
respectively, $P_{A\lambda j}$ is the gross atomic population on atom A from the
atomic $A\lambda$ orbital in the jth molecular orbital, λ is the atomic symmetry at each atomic centre. It is more convenient in practice to use
a comparative method and to use an arbitrary atomic subshell,
$A_0\lambda_0$, as a reference. Then the intensity of the molecular orbital is

$$I_j^{MO} \propto \sum_{A,\lambda} P_{A\lambda j} \, \sigma_{A\lambda}^{AO}/\sigma_{A_0\lambda_0}^{AO}. \tag{6.4}$$

The atomic populations must be calculated by *ab initio* calculations.
Values for the relative cross-sectional areas for various atomic
orbitals can be deduced from the X-ray PE spectra of atom and small
molecules (Table 6.1). With these and values of atomic populations
from *ab initio* calculations, Gelius has obtained good agreement
between computed and experimental spectra for a number of molecules such as benzene, thiophene, sulphur hexafluoride, etc.

These general considerations do not apply to the measurement of
different peaks from the same element and the ratios of non-equivalent atoms can be calculated with ease. It has become common to
resolve broad or poorly resolved bands by computation either with
a simple "curve resolver" or by a larger computer. The peaks are

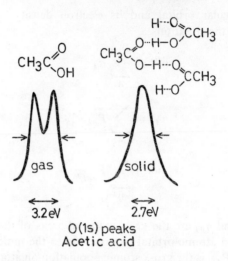

FIG. 6.4. X-ray PE O1s peaks for acetic acid in gas and solid phases. In the solid phase hydrogen bonding equalizes the charges on O to give one broad peak.

taken as symmetrical and a simple computational technique is sufficient. Examples of elemental analyses by ESCA have been given by Siegbahn who has shown, that after calibration graph corrections have been applied to the intensities of peaks in the electron spectrum of silicon carbide, the ratio of the silicon to carbon peaks is $1\cdot0:0\cdot95$ (i.e. 5% discrepancy in $Si:C$ ratio), and for Na_2CO_3 the $Na:C:O$ peak ratios came out to be $1\cdot8:1\cdot0:3\cdot3$ (a 10% discrepancy compared with the correct elemental analysis).[6]

Calibration curves of peak area vs. concentration of the corresponding element in the sample can be constructed and used for the determination of an element in a sample. In their promotional literature AEI show such a curve used to determine fluorine in glass down to a level of less than 3%.

One aspect which has as yet not received proper attention is the effect of contaminants. The effect is hinted at in the literature (surface oil, presumably from the vacuum pump, is used as a calibrant) but not discussed. Presumably, constant impurities can be recognized and allowed for, but it is not difficult to imagine other

TABLE 6.1. ESTIMATED RELATIVE PHOTOIONIZATION CROSS-SECTIONS, $\sigma_{A\lambda}/\sigma A_{o\lambda o}$, FOR ATOMIC VALENCE ELECTRONS.[12]
(The table may be completed for all the atoms, except Ne and Ar, by combining the σ_{AS}/σ_{CS} ratios in the first row with the σ_{AS}/σ_{AP} ratios in the diagonal.)

$\sigma_{A_o\lambda o}$ \ $\sigma_{A\lambda}$	$A\lambda$													
$A_o^o\lambda$	C 2s	C 2p	N 2s	N 2p	O 2s	O 2p	F 2s	F 2p	Ne 2s	Ne 2p	S 3s	S 3p	A 3s	A 3p
C 2s	1		1·2		1·4		2·0				0·47			
C 2p	13	1												
N 2s			1											
N 2p			11*	1										
O 2s					1									
O 2p					8·8	1								
F 2s							1							
F 2p							10*	1						
Ne 2s									1					
Ne 2p									8·7	1				
S 3s											1			
S 3p											1·1	1		
A 3s													1	
A 3p													1·4	1

impurities which could enhance a few peaks in the spectrum thereby vitiating an elemental analysis or quantitative determination. Nevertheless, it seems certain that the analytical applications of X-ray PES will be manifold. Some of them are noted below.

(C) APPLICATION TO THE STUDY OF SURFACES AND SURFACE LAYERS

X-rays can eject electrons from only at most the top 100 A of a solid. Photoelectron spectroscopy is therefore an important technique for studying surfaces and for layers of materials absorbed on the surfaces. Applications in the study of catalysis, surface corrosion and similar processes suggest themselves.

The Varian Company, in their pamphlet on the applications of photoelectron spectroscopy, have for example reported the spectra of fresh and used $CuCr_2O_4$ catalyst (Fig. 6.5). The fresh catalyst spectrum shows two chromium doublets with a peak of each doublet overlapping. The right-hand doublet corresponds to Cr in a negatively charged state, according to existing tables, whilst the left-hand doublet corresponds to positive chromium. On comparing spectra of the fresh and spent catalysts it is evident that the intensity of the left-hand doublet is significantly decreased in the latter, whilst the intensity of the right-hand doublet remains constant.

Linnett and Bordass[13] have studied the valence shell photoelectron spectra of tungsten metal and of tungsten metal with methanol absorbed onto the surface, and although the exact significance of these results is not clear at the present, the potentiality of the method in studying the orbitals involved in bonding absorbed layers onto surfaces is clear.

(D) APPLICATIONS IN POLYMER CHEMISTRY

Whilst various spectroscopic and other techniques can be used to elucidate the molecular formulae of the units making up a polymer, the exact molecular structure may be left uncertain. However photoelectron spectroscopy can sometimes be used to reduce the probable molecular structure from a study of the "chemical shifts"

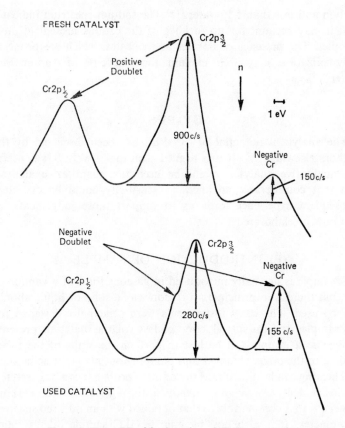

FIG. 6.5. X-ray PE of fresh and used $CuCr_2O_4$ catalyst.

observed. AEI and Varian Associates both refer to spectra of fluorinated polymers to illustrate this possibility. The carbonyl carbon is for instance differentiated from the other carbons in the X-ray spectrum of $[(CF_2)_3FCOCF_3]_n$.

A recent application of ESCA has been in the analysis of "polywater". Davis and Rousseau have shown that samples of anomalous water contain 95% by weight of sodium, potassium, sulphate, carbonate, chloride, nitrate, borates, silicates and traces of organic carbon and less than 5% water.[14] The sodium spectrum indicates that it may account for up to 80% of the cations present in most samples. The presence of borates and silicates, which are prone to polymerization may well explain the viscocity of "anomalous water".

UV-PES

The analytical potential of UV-PES has been discussed by the authors elsewhere.[15] It was argued then that UV-PES was useful for qualitative analysis, might be used for quantitative analysis and that considerable advances in sensitivity could be expected. Subsequent experience leads us to support those judgements, as will now be elaborated.

(E) INTRODUCTION OF SAMPLE

A sample is normally introduced in gaseous form of a vapour or gas, but there is in principle no reason why a solid or liquid should not be used. The early instruments were principally designed for gas samples and the introduction of less volatile materials presents problems; a sample can be lost in part on the walls of the tubes leading to the target chamber and pumping out may take some time and heating can be difficult. Many of these problems can be corrected by instrument design and already a throughput of the Perkin–Elmer PS 16 is comparable to that obtained with an infrared spectrophotometer. It is also possible that a GLC sample inlet system, similar to that used in conjunction with mass spectrometry, could be used. This possibility is being explored.

At present the sample size is largely limited by the difficulties of getting a representative sample into the target chamber. We have obtained spectra on milligram-samples, but it is possible to argue by analogy with the argon gas detector of a GLC that much greater sensitivities could be obtained. The ionization process in that detector is similar to the photoionization process going on in the target chamber and the subsequent counting procedure is much less efficient. One could also deduce that the ultimate sensitivity should be that of mass spectrometry since a similar ionization process is involved. However, in the UV photoelectron spectrometer, there is the problem of preventing excess helium from the discharge zone, entering the target chamber where it increases the pressure which makes the sensitivity appreciably less than that obtainable with mass spectrometry. It does seem though that the sensitivity of photoelectron spectroscopy will be greater than NMR and infrared spectroscopy.

The problems of heating samples is two-fold. Firstly, the sample once introduced into the cold target chamber may condense and contaminate the instrument. Secondly, it is difficult to keep the target chamber and inlet system warm when the material used for their construction is basically stainless steel and they are enclosed in a vacuum. Nevertheless, these problems can be overcome and Ridyard[16] has reported that the spectra of steroids can be obtained.

It is possible to introduce and to obtain a spectrum of a solid sample. Because of the low penetrating power of photons, however, the spectrum is most likely to be that of the molecules adsorbed on the surface. Furthermore, the spectrum will consist of broad peaks because of the molecular disturbances associated with adsorptions.[13] For those engaged in the analysis of surfaces this may be advantageous, but for most it will be preferable to volatilize the sample and to obtain its spectrum in the vapour phase.

(F) CALIBRATION

It cannot be assumed that the energy scale of a spectrometer is either linear or constant, therefore a calibration procedure is essential. The question has recently been reviewed in detail by Lloyd,[17] who makes the following observations:

(i) It is desirable for each instrument to obtain a calibration curve of observed energy vs. true energy (Lloyd's calibration curve is shown in Fig. 6.6). In regions of non-linearity the calibration points used should be as close as possible to the ionization potential being measured, and the instrument scale expansion should be checked with the second calibration point within 1 eV of the first if possible.

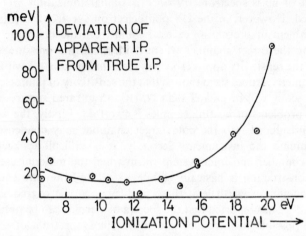

FIG. 6.6. A calibration curve for a PE 15 photoelectron spectrometer.[3]

(ii) The use of gas mixtures for calibration other than Ar–Xe is not recommended because there are near coincidences of ionization peaks which make the lines useless in a mixture and subject to confusion of identification.

(iii) It is also advisable to use as low a pressure of rare gas as possible, less than 10 m torr, since at higher pressures there is a distinct calibration shift of the order of 20 meV for 80 m torr Ar. The pressure effect may even be greater depending on the instrument dimensions.

(iv) It is desirable to admit the calibrant and the compound being measured simultaneously, although this is not always convenient or possible.

(v) The calibrant should not react with the substance being measured.

Lloyd makes no comment on the length of time for which a calibrated instrument remains reasonably constant, but we have found that for most purposes it is not necessary to check more than once a day unless ionization potentials are being accurately measured.

TABLE 6.2. CALIBRATION TABLE FOR UV PES

Line	Electron energy (eV)	Apparent IP (eV)	Line	Electron energy (eV)	Apparent IP (eV)
$CH_3I^2E_{3/2}\gamma$	14·204	7·014	$N_2{}^2\Pi_u(0)$	4·520	16·698
$CH_3I^2E_{1/2}\beta$	12·921	8·926	$Hg^2D_{3/2}$	4·513	16·704
$CH_3I^2E_{3/2}$	11·680	9·538	$N_2{}^2\Pi_u(1)$	4·287	16·930
$CH_3I^2E_{1/2}$	11·052	10·165	$N_2{}^2\Pi_u(2)$	4·059	17·159
$Xe^2P_{3/2}\beta$	10·957	10·261	$N_2{}^2\Pi_u(3)$	3·834	17·384
$Hg^2S_{1/2}$	10·780	10·437	$N_2{}^2\Pi_u(4)$	3·613	17·605
$Xe^2P_{1/2}\beta$	9·651	11·567	$N_2{}^2\Pi_u(5)$	3·395	17·822
$Xe^2P_{1/2}$	9·088	12·130	$N_2{}^2\Sigma_u{}^+$	2·467	18·751
$Kr^2P_{1/2}\beta$	8·421	12·796	$Ne^2P_{3/2}\beta$	1·522	19·695
$Xe^2P_{1/2}$	7·782	13·436	$Ne^2P_{1/2}\beta$	1·425	19·792
$Ar^2P_{3/2}\beta$	7·327	13·890	$O_2{}^2\Sigma_g{}^-(0)$	0·922	20·296
$Kr^2P_{3/2}$	7·218	13·999	$O_2{}^2\Sigma_g{}^-(1)$	0·784	20·433
$Ar^2P_{1/2}\beta$	7·150	14·068	$CH_3I^2E_{3/2}Ly\alpha$	0·661	20·557
$Kr^2P_{1/2}$	6·552	14·665	$O_2{}^2\Sigma_g{}^-(2)$	0·651	20·567
$Hg^2D_{5/2}$	6·378	14·840	$O_2{}^2\Sigma_g{}^-(3)$	0·524	20·693
$N_2{}^2\Sigma_g{}^+$	5·636	15·581	$Hg^2S_{1/2}N(I)$	0·489	20·728
$Ar^2P_{3/2}$	5·458	15·759	$O_2{}^2\Sigma_g{}^-(4)$	0·403	20·815
$Ar^2P_{1/2}$	5·281	15·937	$O_2{}^2\Sigma_g{}^-(5)$	0·286	20·932
			$CH_3I^2E_{1/2}Ly\alpha$	0·033	21·184

The notation for each calibration line is given in the sequence: molecule or atom; ionic state, including the vibrational quantum number where appropriate; exciting line. Where no exciting line is given the He α (584 Å) line is used; β and γ are the 537 Å and 522 Å lines of He, Lyα is the hydrogen Lyman α line at 1216 Å, $N(I)$ is the N triplet at 1135 Å.

γ lines appear at 0·655 eV higher energy (lower IP) than corresponding β lines.

In the latter case it is always desirable to carry out a calibration at the same time as the measurement, i.e. have the calibrant and the sample mixed. The rate of drift obviously depends upon the instrumental condition and possibly extraneous factors, but a typical value is 0·05 eV per day. Lloyd has provided exact calibration points to cover the range from 7 to 21 eV (Table 6.2). Use is made of the lines due to excitation from helium-β and helium-γ radiation. Because of the relatively low intensity of bands excited by these radiations care would be needed in identifying the bands in a mixture. Nevertheless, their use extends the range of calibrant point over that encompassed by most chemical compounds. This is a distinct advance on the relatively narrow range covered by the standard argon–xenon gas mixtures provided as calibrants. For a quick check of the calibration over a fairly wide range the spectrum of carbon disulphide may be run. This has major peaks at IPs 10·068, 10·122, 12·838, 14·478 and 16·196 eV.[18]

(G) QUALITATIVE IDENTIFICATION

Some clue as to the nature of the sample compound may be obtained by a sample visual examination of its photoelectron spectrum. Various bands have characteristic shapes so that the presence, for example, of sharp peaks may indicate the presence of non-bonding electrons and the actual position of these peaks may give some idea as to whether the electrons belong to a halogen, oxygen, nitrogen, phosphorus or sulphur atom within the molecule. Again the presence of a characteristically shaped peak with fine structure may, in the region of 8–11 eV, indicate the presence of π-bonds, and the presence of a broad peak with a few peaks peaking out from it in the region of 12–14 eV may suggest an alkyl group. Individual band shapes of several of the peaks of common contaminants such as water, HCl and nitrogen are readily recognizable and the presence of one may serve to indicate that another of its peaks is hidden under a sample peak and hence is distorting the latter. Unfortunately, although the shapes of the bands of a spectrum are of great aid to an experienced worker, it is not yet possible to codify band shapes in such a way as to provide a routine and certain means of identification either of groups within a molecule or of a molecule itself. The best that can be done is to use correlation diagrams which convey the positions of the peak, its approximate intensity and width. Two such diagrams are shown in Figs. 6.7 and 6.8. In them the peak heights indicate a strong, medium or weak band intensity, the line widths indicate the half-width of a peak and peaks superimposed above a horizontal line indicates a broad band on which several peaks can be identified. The correlation

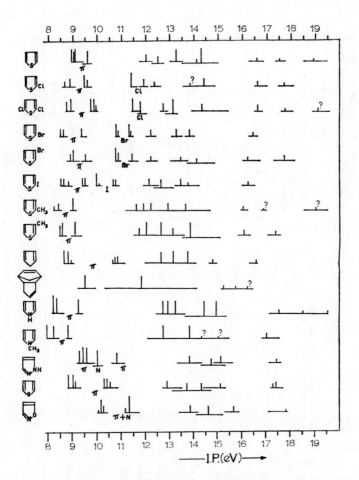

Fig. 6.7. Correlation diagram for 5-membered heterocyclic and related compounds.

diagrams themselves serve to confirm the view that the photoelectron spectrum serves as a qualitative identification of a compound. Naturally, since only a small proportion of the known chemical compounds have been examined by photoelectron spectroscopy, this must remain an interim judgement. The calibration charts do

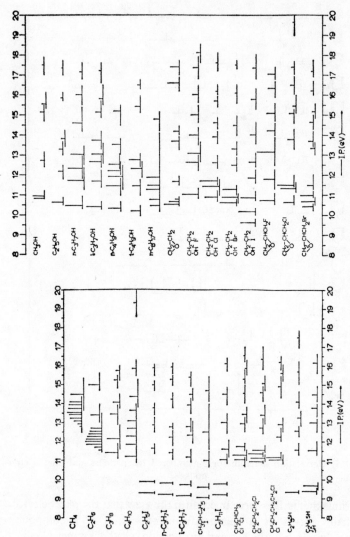

Fig. 6.8. Correlation diagram for various aliphatic compounds.

not serve to indicate the full richness of a photoelectron spectrum, but they condense a lot of information in a convenient manner. They also show that there may be correlation in the sigma bonding region of a spectrum, i.e. 14–20 eV which so far has not been examined in any detailed manner. It is not too surprising that this should be the situation because bands in this region are generally broad and, since they are associated with multicentre σ and π molecular orbitals, it is not very easy to establish correlations of peaks with orbitals. But, in the correlation chart of the heterocyclic compounds (Fig. 6.7) it is obvious that there could be some correlations in this region.

One important feature of a UV–PES spectrum is that isomers are frequently clearly distinguishable, for example, the 2- and 3-substituted thiophenes are quite different (Fig. 6.9).[19] This is quite distinct from the results of mass spectrometry where, for example, the spectra of 2-bromo and 3-bromo thiophene are almost identical. If the photoelectron spectrum can be obtained after a GLC separation, and a cut taken for mass spectrometry and for photoelectron spectrometry, the combined identification provided by the three techniques should be almost certain. Of course, other techniques such as infrared and NMR spectroscopy provide identification of isomers, but it seems probable that photoelectron spectroscopy should be more sensitive than these.

It is also important to remember that the reasons for the difference in the spectra may be quite different and provide useful additional information. This fact is at present obscured to some extent, because the compounds which are being examined by photoelectron spectroscopy are naturally enough the compounds about which we have a lot of information; it would after all be ludicrous to attempt to establish a new technique by comparison of results of uncertain compounds. For example, the first two bands in the spectrum of thiophene are due to ionization from two π-orbitals, one of which has a node through the sulphur atom and one of which does not. Accordingly substitution in the 1- or 2-position leads to a different degree of interactions with these two π-orbitals, and this is clearly shown in the photoelectron spectra of the two isomers. Presumably the extent of interaction, which may be of interest to chemists for

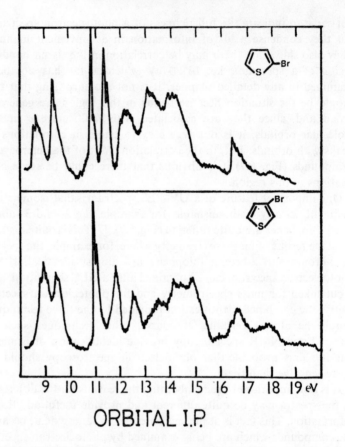

ORBITAL I.P.

FIG. 6.9. UV-PE spectra of 2-bromo- and 3-bromothiophene. π bands in 8·5–9·5 region, 4p "lone-pair" bands in 10·8–11·5 eV region. Degree of splitting showing p-π interaction.

a variety of reasons, is indicated by the changes in the photoelectron spectrum and this extent of interaction is not readily obtained by other techniques. It is also noteworthy that there is no distinct sulphur 3p peak in the photoelectron spectrum of thiophene and this indicates that the sulphur 3p "lone pair" electrons are part of the aromatic sextet. This, of course, is no surprise to contemporary chemists, but it could well have been an interesting result had it not been anticipated by other means. It is probable that information of this kind will, in the future, derive from photoelectron spectroscopy in advance from deductions of other techniques.

(H) MIXTURES

Whereas the photoelectron spectra of individual compounds are distinct it is not generally possible to distinguish the component of a mixture from the photoelectron spectrum of that mixture. In favourable cases, peaks are clearly enough separated so that the components of a simple mixture can be identified; for example, acetone in water or water in acetone can be clearly detected, as can the presence of various sample gases in a mixture and it has been observed already that simple compounds such as water, nitrogen and HCl can readily be detected in the spectrum of other compounds. The situation is thus very similar to that encountered in infrared spectroscopy and it is desirable in most cases to carry out a separation of components of a mixture before obtaining their spectra.

The different volatilities of the components of a mixture may permit resolution of that mixture. The sample can be introduced and continuously pumped out whilst a series of spectra are obtained. Ideally, the first spectrum will contain peaks due to all components, the last will be due solely to the least volatile component and those in between will be progressively denuded of the more volatile components. Obviously this ideal situation will not always pertain, but an example is provided by the spectrum of phosphorus pentachloride (Fig. 6.10).[21] Some water has reacted with it giving HCl and $POCl_3$, which can be detected in the spectrum. This is strengthened by stripping the first spectrum of standard HCl and PCl_5 spectra leaving a $POCl_3$ spectrum. This stripping was carried out by a rather tedious hand computation, which involved digitizing the spectra of suspected components and subtracting them from the first spectrum in proportion suggested by identifiable peak areas. However, it demonstrates that with the aid of a computer or curve resolver, mixtures could be resolved readily and possibly a determination could be effected.

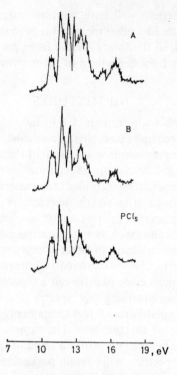

FIG. 6.10. UV-PE spectra obtained from a sample of PCl$_5$ at different times showing separation of mixture by differential volatility. A obtained first, B second, PCl$_5$ is residuum.

Further work on spectrum stripping is in hand.

There are several technical problems to be solved such as which programme is most appropriate in view of the uneven width and irregular shape of the peaks and what constitutes a base line. These are in principle soluble, although it may prove best to use different programmes for different jobs, e.g. spectrum identification, measurement of peak area or fine structure, etc. A more complex problem arises from secondary reactions in the target chamber which change the PE spectrum of a compound slightly, usually by broadening or intensifying a peak. Examples have been mentioned in Chapter

3 under autoionization and another is the nitrogen–carbon dioxide system discussed below, in which spectral peaks vary slightly with sample composition. Of course, it is quite possible that computer-aided spectral analysis will help us to understand more fully the phenomena underlying these secondary reactions.

Spectrum stripping is also proving of value in elucidating another interfering reaction, viz. one which takes place with consumption of sample. An example was noted in a study of phosphorus compounds.[21] Trimethylphosphite was introduced into the instrument, but the spectrum obtained bore no resemblance to that expected. A pair of sharp peaks were reminiscent of the bromine 4p lone-pair peak of methyl bromide, which was subsequently proved to be a product of the reaction between triphenyl phosphite and phosphorus tribromide. It appears that a reaction had taken place between the phosphite and the previous sample (phosphorus pentabromide) although the instrument had been pumped out for 4 days and phosphorus pentabromide could not be detected by the instrument. The instrument was dismantled and valves and pipes cleaned, whereupon the expected spectrum of trimethylphosphite was obtained when a fresh sample was introduced (Fig. 6.11). The exact nature of the reaction and its products is not known with certainty. It is interesting that the spectrum shows no evidence of either trimethyl phosphite, phosphorus pentabromide (or phosphorus tribromide or bromine, which might arise from it). It demonstrates the need for careful experimental techniques backed by an understanding of the underlying theory. Further experiments on these lines should yield considerable and interesting information.

QUANTITATIVE ASPECTS

For quantitative analysis the area under a peak in the spectrum of a given compound should be proportional to the concentration of that compound being irradiated since the ionization efficiency will be dependent on photon flux, orbital ionization cross sectional areas and the number of sample molecules interacting with the photons. It is not known with UV-PES whether this relationship is true. In two of the studies so far carried out,[21] the results are ambiguous

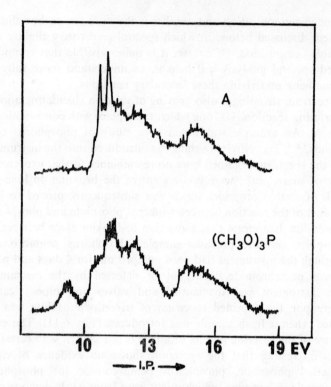

A

$(CH_3O)_3P$

10   13   16   19 EV

⟶ I.P. ⟶

FIG. 6.11. UV-PE spectrum of trimethyl phosphite showing effect of sample interaction. The genuine spectrum has a phosphorus lone pair peak and that of the reaction product(s) has characteristic Br 4p lone pair peaks at ∼ 10·6 eV but bears no resemblance to PBr_5, PBr_3 or Br_2.

because of experimental difficulties. In one of the experiments where mixtures of nitrogen and carbon dioxide were run, there was a correlation between peak height ratios of nitrogen and carbon dioxide and the proportion of nitrogen and carbon dioxide in the mixture. It was found that the needle valve was not fine enough to effect a partial enrichment of one gas in the mixture by Knudsen's effect, and that the manifold pressure and the slit width did not alter the peak height ratios. A major source of variability was the target chamber pressure and another was electronic instability resulting from mains fluctuations and use of an ageing photo-multiplier tube with small plateau. There were deviations from linearity over part of the concentration range which might well be due to secondary reactions in the target chamber.

A big uncertainty in these experiments was the amount of sample which was actually admitted into the target chamber. Better sample control was obtained when water acetone mixtures were weighed into the inlet system. Unfortunately, the results were not reproducible and it was deduced that this was because of the difference in volatilities of water and acetone. In the first instance a spectrum was obtained in which water and acetone could be clearly distinguished and small amounts of water in large amounts of acetone readily detected. After obtaining a spectrum the sample was pumped out and another aliquot introduced. This resulted in a spectrum in which water and acetone were clearly distinguishable, but in which the ratios of the peaks associated with each differed from that obtained in the first run. It was deduced that the water was not completely removed by pumping and formed a capillary layer over the tubes leading into the target chamber so that when the second sample was introduced, the acetone was preferentially absorbed by the water lining the capillary tubes leading to an apparent decrease in the acetone component of the mixture. This obviously may be a general problem and is exacerbated by the differing volatilities of many compounds. It must always be remembered that a trace component in the sample may appear as a major component in the spectrum if the impurity is volatile compared to the compound under examination. It is to be hoped that a different sampling system would overcome several of the difficulties encountered in the quantitative studies and that a quantitative measurement might be provided. Certainly the experiments conducted so far do not rule out the possibility that the technique could be quantitative, although they do indicate that it is not the quantitative technique of choice because the actual identification of peaks and measurements of peak areas is not easy and it seems probable that there are small variations in the peak shapes and sizes due to interactions in the target chamber. These variations would not cause serious difficulties in qualitative identification, but they could result in appreciable error in quantitative determination. Of course a converse of the remarks made above suggest that it might be quite sensitive as a technique for determining minor volatile impurities in samples.

REFERENCES

1. D. HERCULES, *Anal. Chem.*, 1970, **42** (1), 20A.
2. B. J. LINDBERG, K. MANRIM, G. JOHANSSON, U. GELIUS, A. FAHLMAN, C. NORDLING and K. SIEGBAHN, Uppsala University Inst. Physics, UUIP-638, 1970.
3. K. SIEGBAHN *et al.*, *ESCA—Atomic, Molecular and Solid State Structure Studied by Means of Electron Spectroscopy*. Uppsala 1967, New Ed. to be published by North-Holland, Amsterdam.
4. K. SIEGBAHN *et al.*, *ESCA Applied to Free Molecules*, North-Holland, Amsterdam, 1969.
5. K. SIEGBAHN, *Phil. Trans. Roy. Soc. Lond. Ser.* A., 1970, **268**, 33.
6. K. SIEGBAHN, *Nature*, 1966, **210**, 4.
7. K. SEIGBAHN, *Z. Phys.* 1964, **138**, 443.
8. J. J. JACK and D. M. HERCULES, *Anal. Chem.*, 1971, **43**, 729.
9. U. GELIUS, P. F. HEDEN, J. HEDMAN, B. J. LINDBERG, R. MANNE, R. NORDBERG, C. NORDLING and K. SIEGBAHN, Uppsala Univ. Institute of Physics, UUIP-714, 1970.
10. C. D. COOK, K. Y. WAN, U. GELIUS, K. HAMRIN, G. JOHANSSON, E. OLSON, H. SIEGBAHN, C. NORDLING and K. SIEGBAHN, Uppsala Univ. Institute of Physics, UUIP-717, 1970.
11. C. J. ALLAN and K. SIEGBAHN, Uppsala Univ. Institute of Physics, UUIP-754 (1971).
12. U. GELIUS, Uppsala Univ. Institute of Physics, UUIP-753 (1971).
13. W. T. BORDASS and J. W. LINNETT, *Nature*, 1969, 222.
14. DAVIS and ROUSSEAU, *Chem. & Eng. News*,
15. D. BETTERIDGE and A. D. BAKER, *Anal. Chem.*, 1970, **42** (1), 43A.
16. N. RIDYARD, Private communication.
17. D. R. LLOYD, *J. Phys. E. Sci. Instr.*, 1970, **3**, 629.
18. D. W. TURNER, C. BAKER, A. D. BAKER and C. R. BRUNDLE, *Molecular Photoelectron Spectroscopy*, Wiley, London, 1970. pp. 98–103.
19. A. D. BAKER, D. BETTERIDGE, N. R. KEMP and R. E. KIRBY, *Anal. Chem.*, 1970, **42**, 1064.
20. A. D. BAKER, D. BETTERIDGE, N. R. KEMP and R. E. KIRBY, *Anal. Chem.*, 1971, **43**, 375.
21. D. BETTERIDGE, M. THOMPSON, A. D. BAKER and N. R. KEMP, Unpublished work.
22. D. BETTERIDGE and N. R. KEMP, Unpublished work.

CHAPTER 7

OTHER FORMS OF ELECTRON SPECTROSCOPY

AUGER ELECTRON SPECTROSCOPY (AS)

In the Auger effect, electrons are emitted from a substance in a radiationless transition from an excited state produced by an impacting beam of X-ray photons or electrons. Auger electron spectroscopy is concerned with the measurement of the energies and relative intensities of these ejected electrons. AS therefore differs from X-ray PES (ESCA) in that it looks at electrons ejected in a secondary rather than in a primary step. The energy of an Auger electron will depend only upon the electron energy levels of the states involved in the secondary process, and will be quite independent of the energy of the impacting species (in contrast to ESCA). In other words, the energy of electrons released in AS are determined solely by the nature of the atoms from which they originated, and their chemical environment. There is therefore no need to use a monochromatic source to study Auger spectra.

The primary process involved in AS is the absorption of energy by the bombarded material, and the ejection of an electron out of an inner orbital. The "positive hole" created is then filled by an electron falling back into the vacancy, thereby providing sufficient energy to eject the "Auger electron".

Both Auger and "direct" ionization processes can take place in the collision zone of an X-ray photoelectron spectrometer, and thus the "ESCA" spectrum can reveal information on both types of processes (see Chapter 3). It is easy to distinguish which of the peaks in an "ESCA" spectrum relate to Auger processes, however, since their positions will be invariant of any changes made in the incident X-ray wavelength.

Although Auger spectra can be excited by X-radiation, it is normal to use an electron gun for the specific study of this type of phenomenon, since more intense spectra are obtained, and furthermore, the only discrete peaks appearing in the electron impact induced spectra are due to Auger electrons.

AS is particularly useful for studying compounds containing light atoms ($Z \leqslant 12$) because for these the ejection of an Auger electron is the major relaxation process for the excited states produced by the creation of an inner shell vacancy—the other possibility, fluorescent decay, being relatively unimportant. For heavy atoms, the converse is true, and this implies that the Auger method of relaxation will be less significant since the Auger and fluorescent relaxation processes are complementary.

The presence of peaks at certain energies in the Auger electron distribution spectrum can imply in a similar way to peaks in an ESCA spectrum that certain atoms are present in the emitting material. Chemical shifts are also observed in AS as the environment of an atom is changed, but in general, the shift mechanism will be more complex than that operating in ESCA, since it is a function of more than one energy level. Provided, however, that all the levels involved in an Auger process are inner-shell type, shifts similar to ESCA shifts may be observed,[1] but if the upper levels are valence shell type no simple correlations between Auger shifts and atomic charges, etc., are to be expected owing to the complex nature of the changes existing between the valence orbitals of different molecules.[2]

The terminology used to describe an Auger process encompasses three letters written consecutively which describe:

(1) the shell in which the primary vacancy is created;
(2) the shell from which an electron falls back into the vacant "positive hole";
(3) the shell from which the Auger electron is ejected.

Thus a KL_IL_{II} Auger process, translated into atomic orbital terms, implies the initial creation of a K-shell (1s) vacancy, the falling back of an electron from the L_I shell (2s) and the ejection of a L_{II} electron (2p) (Fig. 7.1).

Both solid-state and vapour-phase Auger spectra can be obtained. As was the case with ESCA, sharper peaks can be obtained from vapour phase spectra,[2,3] and this higher resolving power results in gaseous Auger spectra containing very many resolved peaks. Relatively few molecules apart from simple atoms and molecules have been studied by vapour-phase AS because of the complexity of their spectra.

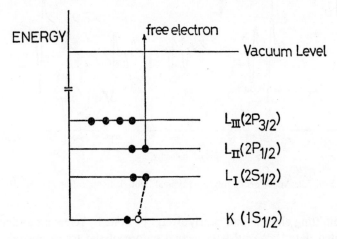

FIG. 7.1. Schematic representation of a KL_IL_{II} Auger process.

Solid-state studies, however, have been very prevalent, and indeed, Auger spectroscopy is one of the most powerful techniques currently available for studying the surface layers of materials. Surface contaminants can often be shown up by virtue of the Auger electron spectra they excite when bombarded with electrons. Some examples cited in a review by Harris[4] are the identification of phosphorus as a residue of a plating procedure, and of contaminants in semiconducting materials. The technique is also sensitive to residues left on surfaces by various solvents, and has applications in fields such as metallurgy for studying the concentrations of various materials at fractures, etc.[4]

Assignment of a particular peak in an Auger spectrum to a particu-

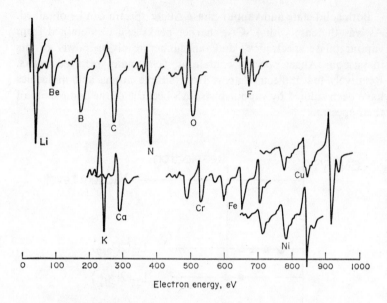

Fɪɢ. 7.2. Auger peaks for some typical light elements (after Harris[4]).

lar emitting element can nearly always be done by referring to documented data,[1,5] whilst the actual nature of the transition taking place can often be inferred from X-ray tables. [5,6]

There is a consensus of opinion that when AS is applied to surface studies, the penetration depth is limited to the top ten monolayers, or less, and is thus always less than a few hundred angstroms. This penetration depth can be varied by altering the exciting energy and the take-off angle.

A typical Auger solid-state spectrum consists of discrete peaks standing out from a broad background spectrum arising from the multiple scattering of the Auger and other ejected electrons[7] (see Fig. 7.2). Since most experimentalists to date have used retarding grid electron energy analysers (see Chapter 2) to study Auger processes, their primary data is an integrated energy distribution curve, differentiation of which yields the actual electron spectrum. The use of focusing analysers in Auger spectrometers is an attractive possibility, which is now receiving attention. Much higher resolving power and sensitivity can be obtained by using such an analyser in conjunction with an electron multiplier detector (cf. PES and ESCA), and further-more the electron spectrum is obtained as primary data. In practice, the composition of layers as thin as 0·01 monolayer or less may be determined, but because such thin layers are involved, extreme care will have to be taken in surface preparation and in the cleanliness of the vacuum system used.

ELECTRON-IMPACT ENERGY-LOSS SPECTROSCOPY (EIS)

Electrons can, as pointed out in previous sections, eject planetary electrons from atoms and molecules with which they collide, either by direct ionization, by autoionization, or by the Auger effect. However, impacting electrons can also impart sufficiently low energies to the bombarded molecules to merely promote bound electrons into orbitals of higher energy, rather than to eject them completely. In such a case, the original impacting electron is scattered with a lower energy than it originally possessed. Quantum rules require that excitation processes will only occur when the difference in energies, ΔE, between the excited and unexcited molecular states is equal to the difference in energy between the primary and scattered impacting electron:

$$\Delta E = E_p - E_s. \tag{7.1}$$

The examination of the energy spectrum of the scattered electrons will therefore reveal discrete peaks giving the excitation energies of the molecular system being examined provided that E_p is held constant.

Since the technique covers the energy range of visible, ultraviolet, and vacuum ultraviolet absorption spectroscopy, it provides infor-mation which closely parallels that given by these techniques. An advantage is that a wide energy span is covered in one instrument rather than two or three. The different selection rules governing photon impact and electron impact processes do nevertheless result in their being differences in the detail of electron impact and optical spectra over the same energy region.

Most EIS studies have been carried out on gases[8,9]—some typical spectra are shown in Fig. 7.3—and have usually been carried out by physicists or spectroscopists seeking to answer fundamental physical or spectroscopic problems. Discrete electron energy losses may occur on the bombardment of solids owing to processes such as phonon

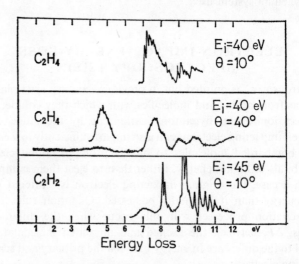

FIG. 7.3. Some typical electron-impact energy-loss spectra. Peaks correspond to the excitation energies of the molecular system under examination. E_i refers to the energy of the incident electrons, and θ to the scattering angle at which the measurements were taken.

and plasmon excitations as well as the expected band-to-band electronic transitions (see ref. 7 for a description of the phonon and plasmon type processes).

EIS is now being applied to analytical problems, both to detect trace amounts of gases, and to study species absorbed onto surfaces. In the gas analysis work, it was claimed that 0·2 nanogram levels of argon and 0·2 picogram levels of helium were detectable.[10] Propst and Piper[11] used monochromatized low-energy (4·5 eV) electron beams to study absorbed species, enabling them to work at a resolving power of about 0·05 eV, more than two orders of magnitude better than that obtained in most other solid state studies. They observed discrete energy losses in the 0 to 800 meV region for absorbed water, carbon monoxide, hydrogen and nitrogen, and related them to the excitation of vibrational modes in these gases. The actual values of the frequencies enabled deductions to be made about the state of the absorbed species, e.g. no H—H or N—N vibrations were observed in the cases of adsorbed hydrogen and nitrogen, indicating that these gases are completely dissociated. The low vibrational frequencies observed in these cases were suggested to be due to the vibrations of an adsorbed atom in the surface bond.

ION-NEUTRALIZATION SPECTROSCOPY
(INS)

INS is a branch of Auger spectroscopy which has been developed by Hagstrum.[12] In INS the sample material is bombarded with monoenergetic rare-gas ions in place of electrons or photons. The bombarding ion becomes neutralized by acquiring an electron from a surface species, and the energy released is sufficient to eject an Auger electron. INS appears to be a genuine surface technique[7,15] and has been applied to clean metal surfaces to yield the band structure,[13] and to study the molecular orbitals responsible for the chemisorption of species onto surfaces.[14,15]

Although the apparatus used to study INS, and the procedures used for the analysis of the primary data are considerably more complex than in AS, it is probably fair to say that the full potential of the method has only been touched upon to-date. Simplifications in experimentation can be expected,[7,16] which should lead to a new insight into interactions at surfaces.

ANGULAR DISTRIBUTIONS OF
PHOTOELECTRONS

The angular distribution of electrons ejected from gaseous atoms and molecules through collisions with monoenergetic photons has

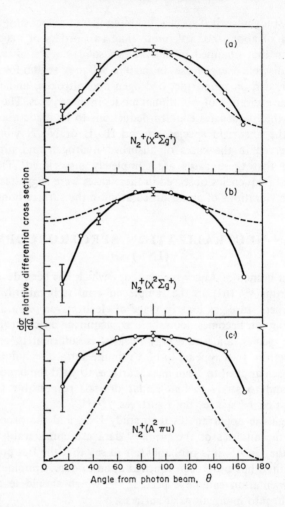

FIG. 7.4. Differential angular distributions of photoelectrons from nitrogen gas: (a) formation of the $\tilde{X}\,^2\Sigma_g{}^+$ ionic state by 21·2 eV photons; (b) formation of the $\tilde{X}^2\Sigma_g$ ionic state by 16·67 and 16·85 eV photons; (c) formation of the $\tilde{A}^2\pi_u$ state by 21·2 eV photons. The solid line is the experimental curve theoretical or $\sin^2\theta$ distribution.[26]

aroused considerable interest in recent years. In principle the form of the angular distribution should differ according to the symmetry of the orbital from which the electrons were ejected. Both theoretical calculations[17-22] and experimental observations[23-27] of angular distributions of photoelectrons have been reported. One of the difficulties on the experimental side is that the light used to ionize the atoms and molecules is not plane polarized, but this has been taken into account by McGowan et al.[26] At present, however, there is only very limited agreement between theoretical predictions and experimental results. Distributions do show marked variations, nevertheless, depending upon the orbital originally occupied by the electrons. Thus Fig. 7.4 shows the observed distributions for electrons from the three highest occupied orbitals of nitrogen gas. Clearly there is considerable potential for studies of this type.

OTHER PHOTOELECTRON TECHNIQUES

Two other new techniques based upon the measurement of electrons ejected from molecules by a photoionization process have developed out of the context of electron spectrometry. In the first of these techniques[28] both the ions and the electrons formed during photoionization are collected. The ejected electrons are sent into an electron energy analyser, and the ions into a mass spectrometer. Coincidence techniques are employed so that the energy spectrum of only those electrons ejected from sample molecules when ions of a chosen mass are simultaneously produced is obtained. Alternatively a mass spectrum of ions in coincidence with electrons of a specific energy could be obtained. Results from such experiments are important for studying fragmentation processes.

In the second of the new techniques[29-33] electrons ejected from molecules by photoionization are again sent into an energy analyser and detected. However, unlike conventional photoelectron spectrometry, this new technique employs a variable energy source. The electron energy analyser is set to collect only electrons of a specified kinetic energy (usually zero energy or "threshold" electrons), and the photon energy is continually varied by means of a scanning monochromator. The spectrum obtained therefore consists of electron count rate plotted as y-axis against energy of incident photons as x-axis. The information afforded by this technique is in many ways identical to that given by conventional photoelectron spectroscopy but can in addition indicate anomalies arising out of autoionization processes (see preceding chapters).

REFERENCES

1. K. SIEGBAHN et al., Electron Spectroscopy for Chemical Analysis, Almquist & Wiksells, 1967.
2. K. SIEGBAHN et al., ESCA Applied to Free Molecules, North-Holland, Amsterdam, 1970.
3. T. A. CARLSON, W. E. MODDEMAN, B. P. PULLEN and M. O. KRAUSE, Chem. Phys. Lett., 1970, 5, 390.
4. L. HARRIS, Analyt. Chem., 1968, 40, 24A.
5. P. W. PALMBERG and T. W. RHODIN, J. Appl. Phys., 1968, 39, 2425.
6. R. D. HILL, F. L. CHURCH and T. W. MIHELICH, Rev. Sci. Instr., 1952, 23, 523.
7. C. R. BRUNDLE, Surface and Defect Properties of Solids, Vol. I, Chemical Society, Specialist Periodical Report, to be published.
8. S. TRAJMAR, J. K. RICE and A. KUPPERMAN, Advances in Chemical Physics, 1970, XVIII, 15.
9. R. S. BERRY, Ann, Rev. Phys. Chem., 1970, 20, 357.
10. The Editor's Column, Analyt. Chem., 1968, 40, 99A.
11. F. M. PROPST and T. C. PIPER, J. Vac. Science and Tech., 1966, 4, 53,
12. H. D. HAGSTRUM, Phys. Rev., 1966, 150, 495.
13. H. D. HAGSTRUM and G. E. BECKER, Phys. Rev. Lett., 1966, 16, 230.
14. H. D. HAGSTRUM and G. E. BECKER, Phys. Rev. Lett., 1969, 22, 1054.
15. H. D. HAGSTRUM and G. E. BECKER, J. Chem. Phys., to be published.
16. H. D. HAGSTRUM and G. E. BECKER, work quoted in ref. 7 which is to be published; H. D. HAGSTRUM, J. Res. Nat. Bur. Stds., 1970, 14A, 433.
17. J. COOPER and R. N. ZARE, J. Chem. Phys., 1968, 48, 942.
18. S. H. LIN, Canad. J. Phys., 1968, 46, 2720.
19. J. W. COOPER and S. T. MANSON, Phys. Rev., 1969, 177, 157.
20. J. C. TULLY, R. S. BERRY and B. J. DALTON, Phys. Rev., 1968, 176, 95.
21. B. SCHNEIDER and R. S. BERRY, Phys. Rev., 1969, 182, 141.
22. A. D. BUCKINGHAM, B. J. ORR and J. M. SICHEL, Phil. Trans. Roy. Soc. London, 1970, A 268, 147.
23. J. BERKOWITZ and H. EHRHARDT, Phys. Lett., 1966, 21, 531.
24. J. BERKOWITZ, H. EHRHARDT and T. TEKAAT, Z. Physik, 1967, 200, 69.
25. J. W. MCGOWAN, D. A. VROOM and A. R. COMEAUX, Chem. Phys. Lett., 1969 3, 476.
26. J. W. MCGOWAN, D. A. VROOM and A. R. COMEAUX, J. Chem. Phys., 1969, 51, 5626.
27. J. A. R. SAMSON, Phil. Trans. Roy. Soc. London, 1970, A 268, 141.

28. B. BREHM and E. VON PUTTKAMER, in *Advances in Mass Spectrometry* (published by Institute of Petroleum, 1968).
29. W. B. PEATMAN, T. B. BARNE and E. W. SCHLAG, *Chem. Phys. Lett.*, 1969, **3**, 492,
30. D. VILLAREJO, R. STOCKBAUER and M. G. INGHRAM, *J. Chem. Phys.*, 1968, **48**, 3342.
31. D. VILLAREJO, *J. Chem. Phys.*, **48**, 4014, 1968.
32. D. VILLAREJO, R. STOCKBAUER and M. G. INGHRAM, *J. Chem. Phys.*, 1969, **50**, 4599.
33. R. STOCKBAUER and M. G. INGHRAM, *J. Chem. Phys.*, 1971, **54**, 2242.

INNER-SHELL ORBITAL IONIZATION POTENTIALS FOR ATOMS

ELECTRON BINDING ENERGIES (eV)

Element	$1s_{1/2}$ K	$2s_{1/2}$ L_{I}	$2p_{1/2}$ L_{II}	$2p_{3/2}$ L_{III}	$3s_{1/2}$ M_{I}	$3p_{1/2}$ M_{II}	$3p_{3/2}$ M_{III}	$3d_{3/2}$ M_{IV}	$3d_{5/2}$ M_{V}	$4s_{1/2}$ N_{I}	$4p_{1/2}$ N_{II}	$4p_{3/2}$ N_{III}	$4d_{3/2}$ N_{IV}	$4d_{5/2}$ N_{V}	$4f_{5/2}$ N_{VI}	$4f_{7/2}$ N_{VII}
1 H	14															
2 He	25															
3 Li	55															
4 Be	111															
5 B	188[1]															
6 C	285[1]															
7 N	399[1,9]															
8 O	532[1]	24[2]														
9 F	686[1]	31														
10 Ne	867	45														
11 Na	1072[1]	63[3]	31													
12 Mg	1305[1]	89[3]	52													
13 Al	1560[1]	118[3]	74	73												
14 Si	1839[1]	149[3]	100	99												
15 P	2149[1]	189[3]	136	135												
16 S	2472[1]	229[3]	165	164	16											
17 Cl	2823[1]	270[3]	202	200	18											
18 A	3203	320[3]	247	245	25											
19 K		377[3]	297	294	34	18										
20 Ca		438[3]	350	347	44	26										
21 Sc		500[3]	407	402	54	32										
22 Ti		564[3]	461	455	59	34										
23 V		628[3]	520	513	66	38										
24 Cr		695[3]	584	575	74	43										
25 Mn		769[3]	652	641	84	49										
26 Fe		846[3]	723	710	95	56										
27 Co		926[3]	794	779	101	60										
28 Ni		1008[3]	872	855	112	68										
29 Cu		1096[3]	951	931	120	74										
30 Zn		1194	1044	1021	137	87										
31 Ga		1298	1143	1116	158	107	103	18								
32 Ge		1413[6]	1249	1217	181	129	122	29								
33 As		1527	1359	1323	204	147	141	41								
34 Se		1654	1476	1436	232	168	162	57								
35 Br		1782[7]	1596[7]	1550[7]	257	189	182	70	69	24						
36 Kr		1921	1727	1675	289*	223	214	89		27						
37 Rb					322	248	239	112	111	30						
38 Sr					358	280	269	135	133	38	20					
39 Y					395	313	301	160	158	46	26					
40 Zr					431	345	331	183	180	52	29					

ELECTRON BINDING ENERGIES (eV) (cont.)

	$1s_{1/2}$ K	$2s_{1/2}$ L$_\mathrm{I}$	$2p_{1/2}$ L$_\mathrm{II}$	$2p_{3/2}$ L$_\mathrm{III}$	$3s_{1/2}$ M$_\mathrm{I}$	$3p_{1/2}$ M$_\mathrm{II}$	$3p_{3/2}$ M$_\mathrm{III}$	$3d_{3/2}$ M$_\mathrm{IV}$	$3d_{5/2}$ M$_\mathrm{V}$	$4s_{1/2}$ N$_\mathrm{I}$	$4p_{1/2}$ N$_\mathrm{II}$	$4p_{3/2}$ N$_\mathrm{III}$	$4d_{3/2}$ N$_\mathrm{IV}$	$4d_{5/2}$ N$_\mathrm{V}$	$4f_{5/2}$ N$_\mathrm{VI}$	$4f_{7/2}$ N$_\mathrm{VII}$
41 Nb					469	379	363	208	205	58	34					
42 Mo					505	410	393	230	227	62	35					
43 Tc					544*	445	425	257	253	68*	39					
44 Ru					585	483	461	284	279	75	43					
45 Rh					627	521	496	312	307	81	48					
46 Pd					670	559	531	340	335	86	56	51				
47 Ag					717	602	571	373	367	95	62					
48 Cd					770	651	617	411	404	108	67					
49 In					826	702	664	451	443	122	77					
50 Sn					884	757	715	494	485	137	89					
51 Sb					944	812	766	537	528	152	99		32			
52 Te					1006	870	819	582	572	168	110		40			
53 I					1072	931	875	631	620	186	123		50*			
54 Xe					1145*	999	937	685*	672	208*	147		63*			
55 Cs					1217	1065	998	740	726	231	172	162	79	77		
56 Ba					1293	1137	1063	796	781	253	192	180	93	90		
57 La					1362	1205	1124	849	832	271	206	192	99			
58 Ce					1435	1273	1186	902	884	290	224	208	111			
59 Pr					1511	1338	1243	951	931	305	237	218	114			
60 Nd					1576	1403	1298	1000	978	316	244	225	118			
61 Pm					1650*	1472*	1357*	1052*	1027*	331*	255*	237*	121*			
62 Sm					1724	1542	1421	1107	1081	347	267	249	130			
63 Eu					1800	1614	1481	1161	1131	360	284	257	134			
64 Gd					1881	1689	1544	1218	1186	376	289	271	141			
65 Tb					1968	1768	1612	1276	1242	398	311	286	148			
66 Dy					2047	1842	1676	1332	1295	416	332	293	154			
67 Ho					2128	1923	1741	1391	1351	436	343	306	161			
68 Er					2207	2006	1812	1453	1409	449	366	320	177	168		
69 Tm					2307	2090	1885	1515	1468	472	386	337	180			
70 Yb					2397	2172	1949	1576	1527	487	396	343	197	184		
71 Lu					2491	2264	2024	1640	1589	506	410	359	205	195		
72 Hf					2601	2365	2108	1716	1662	538	437	380	224	214	19[17]	18[17]
73 Ta					2708	2469[12]	2194[12]	1793[12]	1735[12]	566	465	405	242	230	27[17]	25[17]
74 W					2820	2575[12]	2281[12]	1872[12]	1810[12]	595	492	426	259	246	37[17]	34[17]
75 Re					2932	2682[12]	2367[12]	1949[12]	1883[12]	625	518	445	274	260	47[17]	45[17]
76 Os					3049	2792[12]	2458[12]	2031[12]	1960[12]	655	547	469	290	273	52[17]	50[17]
77 Ir					3174	2909[12]	2551[12]	2116[12]	2041[12]	690	577	495	312	295	63[17]	60[17]
78 Pt					3298[20]	3027[20]	2646[20]	2202[20]	2121[20]	724[20]	608[20]	519[20]	331[20]	314[20]	74[20]	70[27]
79 Au					3425[12]	3150[12]	2743[12]	2291[12]	2206[12]	759	644	546	352	334	87[17]	83[17]
80 Hg					3562	3279	2847[12]	2385[12]	2295[12]	800	677	571	379	360	103[17]	99[17]

(continued overleaf)

ELECTRON BINDING ENERGIES (eV) (cont.)

	1s1/2 K	2s1/2 LI	2p1/2 LII	2p3/2 LIII	3s1/2 MI	3p1/2 MII	3p3/2 MIII	3d3/2 MIV	3d5/2 MV	4s1/2 NI	4p1/2 NII	4p3/2 NIII	4d3/2 NIV	4d5/2 NV	4f5/2 NVI	4f7/2 NVII
81 Tl					3704	3416[12]	2957[12]	2485[12]	2390[12]	846	722	609	407	386	122[17]	118[17]
82 Pb					3851	3554[12]	3067[12]	2586[12]	2484[12]	894	764	645	435	413	143[17]	138[17]
83 Bi					3999[12]	3697[12]	3177[12]	2688[12]	2580[12]	939[12]	806[12]	679[12]	464[12]	440[12]	163[17]	158[17]
84 Po					4149	3854	3302	2798	2683	995	851	705	500	473	184*	
85 At					4317*	4008	3426	2909	2787	1042*	886	740	533	507*	210*	
86 Rn										1097*	929*	768	567	541*	238*	
87 Fr										1153*	980	810	603	577	268*	
88 Ra										1208*	1058	879	636	603	299	
89 Ac										1269*	1080	890	675	639*	319*	
90 Th										1330[13]	1168[13]	968[13]	714[13]	677[13]	344[13]	335[13]
91 Pa										1387	1224	1007	743	708	371	360
92 U										1442[14]	1272[14]	1045[14]	780[14]	738[14]	392	381
93 Np										1501[15]	1328[15]	1087[15]	817[15]	773[15]	415[15]	404[15]
94 Pu										1558	1377	1120	849[16]	801[16]	422	
95 Am										1617	1412	1136+	879	828	440+	

1. S. HAGSTRÖM, and S. E. KARLSSON, Arkiv Fysik, 1964, 26, 451.
2. A. FAHLMAN, K. HAMRIN, R. NORDBERG, C. NORDLING, and K. SIEGBAHN, Phys. Rev. Lett. 1965, 14, 127.
3. R. NORDBERG, K. HAMRIN, A. FAHLMAN, C. NORDLING, and K. SIEGBAHN, Z. Phys. 1966, 192, 462.
4. E. SOKOLOWSKI, Arkiv Fysik, 1959, 15, 1.
5. A. FAHLMAN, S. HAGSTRÖM, K. HAMRIN, R. NORDBERG, C. NORDLING, and K. SIEGBAHN, Arkiv Fysik, 1966, 31, 479.
6. C. NORDLING, Arkiv Fysik, 1959, 15, 397.
7. I. ANDERSSON, and S. HAGSTRÖM, Arkiv Fysik, 1964, 27, 161.
8. A. FAHLMAN, O. HÖRNFELDT, and C. NORDLING, Arkiv Fysik, 1962, 23, 75.
9. P. BERGVALL, O. HÖRNFELDT, and C. NORDLING, Arkiv Fysik, 1960, 17, 113.
10. P. BERGVALL, and S. HAGSTRÖM, Arkiv Fysik, 1960, 17, 61.
11. S. HAGSTRÖM, Z. Phys., 1966, 178, 82.
12. A. FAHLMAN, and S. HAGSTRÖM, Arkiv Fysik, 1964, 27, 69.
* Abstracted from ref. 2.12. Some outer and inner IPs have been omitted.

APPENDIX 2

FIRST IONIZATION POTENTIALS OF
ATOMS, eV

1	2	3	4	5	6	7	8	9	10	11	12	13	14	15	16	17	18
H 13·6																	He 24·6
Li 5·4	Be 9·3											B 8·3	C 11·3	N 14·5	O 13·6	F 17·4	Ne 21·6
Na 5·1	Mg 7·6											Al 6·0	Si 8·1	P 10·5	S 10·4	Cl 13·0	A 15·8
K 4·3	Ca 6·1	Sc 6·5	Ti 6·8	V 6·7	Cr 6·8	Mn 7·4	Fe 7·9	Co 7·9	Ni 7·6	Cu 7·7	Zn 9·4	Ga 6·0	Ge 7·9	As 9·8	Se 9·8	Br 11·8	Kr 14·0
Rb 4·2	Sr 5·7	Y 6·4	Zr 6·8	Nb 6·9	Mo 7·1	Tc 7·3	Ru 7·4	Rh 7·5	Pd 8·3	Ag 7·6	Cd 9·0	In 5·8	Sn 7·3	Sb 8·6	Te 9·0	I 10·5	Xe 12·1
Cs 3·9	Ba 5·2	La 5·6	Hf 7	Ta 7·9	W 8·0	Re 7·9	Os 8·7	Ir 9	Pt 9·0	Au 9·2	Hg 10·4	Tl 6·1	Pb 7·6	Bi 7·3	Po 8·4	At —	Rn 10·7
Fr —	Ra 5·3	Ac 6·9															

Taken from C. E. Moore, *Atomic Energy Levels*, Vol. III, Circular of the Nat. Bur. Stand. 467, Washington, 1958.

APPENDIX 3

SELECTED APPROXIMATE ORBITAL IONIZATION POTENTIALS OF SOME SMALL MOLECULES, eV

	σ 1s	σ 2s	σ 2p	π 2p	π 2p
H_2	15·5				
N_2		18·8	15·6	17	
O_2			18·2	16·1	12·1
CO		19·7	14·0	16·9	
NO		19·3	16·5, 18·3	17	9·3

	σ	Lone pair
HF	19·9	16·4
HCl	16·5	12·8
HBr	15·5	11·8
HI	14·1	10·6
H_2O	18·8, 14·8	12·6
H_2S	15·4, 13·4	10·5
H_3N	21·2, 15·8	10·9
H_3P	21·2, 13·0	9·9

$H_2C = O$ 16·3 (—CH_2)   15·9 (all atom)   14·1 (π c=o) 10·9   (O lone pair
$H_2C = CH_2$ 15·6, 14·5, 12·4   (σ C—C, C—H)   10·5 (π c=c)
Benzene, see Table 4.1.

These values have been selected to provide some guidance on the ordering of orbitals of more commonly encountered elements in their compounds. As is clear from the text, each molecular orbital is a mixture of atomic orbitals and its energy is appreciably affected by molecular environment. Nevertheless, these values should provide some guidance as to the positions of peaks due to these elements and to the likely extent of interaction of lone pair orbitals.

163

APPENDIX 4

SELECTED VALUES OF INNER-SHELL BINDING ENERGIES MEASURED BY PHOTOELECTRON SPECTROSCOPY

CARBON 1s

Binding energy range (eV)[†]	Compounds[‡]
290–291	C_6H_6, C_2H_6, C_2H_4, CH_4
291–292	C_2H_2, $CH_3CH_2NH_2$, CH_3Br
292–293	CH_3CH_2Cl, $HC=N—CH=N—NH$, CH_3CH_2OH, CH_3Cl, CH_3OH, $CH_3CH_2O(CO)CH_3$
293–294	CS_2, CH_2Br_2, HCN, $SC(NH_2)_2$, CH_3F, $H_2C=O$, $(CH_3CHO)_3$, $(CH_3)_2C=O$, CH_2Cl_2
294–295	C_6Cl_6, C_6F_6, $(NH_2)_2\,C=O$
295–296	$CHCl_3$, CH_3COH_2, $HC(OCH_3)_3$
296–297	CCl_4, CO
297–298	$O=C\,(OEt)Cl$, $O=C\,(OCH_3)_2$, CO_2
298–299	$Cl_2F\,CCClF_2$, ClF_2CCCl_2F, CF_3COCH_4
299–300	CHF_3, COF_2
300–301	
301–302	CF_4

†Precise values can be found in ref. 2.12.
‡Gases.

For compounds containing more than one carbon atom, the values refer to the italicized atom.

164

NITROGEN 1s†

Compound‡	Binding energy (eV)	Compound	Binding energy (eV)
$[Rh(NH_3)_6]\,(NO_3)_3$	407·3	$Na_2[Fe(CN)_5NO]\cdot2H_2O$	398·2
trans-$[Co(en)_2(NO_2)_2]$	406·8	$NaNO_3$	407·4
NO_3		$NaNO_2$	404·1
p-$NO_2C_6H_4CONH_2$	405·9		
$[Rh(NH_3)_5NO_2]Br_2$	404·4	$Na_2(ONNO_2)$	403·9
$Co(NH_3)_3(NO_2)_3$	404·1	$Na_2(ONNO_2)$	400·9
$[Co(NH_3)_5NO_2]Cl_2$	404·0	$Na(NNN)$	403·7
$K[Co(NH_3)_2(NO_2)_4]$	404·0	$Na(NNN)$	399·3
$K_3CO(NO_2)_6$	404·0	$Na_2N_2O_2$	401·3
trans-$[Co(NH_3)_4(NO_2)_2]$	403·9	KCN	399·0
SO_4		$KOCN$	398·3
trans-$[Co(en)_2(NO_2)_2]$	403·8		
NO_3		p-$HOC_6H_4NO_2$	405·3
$Na_2[Fe(CN)_5NO]\,2H_2O$	403·3		
S_4N_4	402·1	$C_6H_5NO_2$	405·1
$[Co(NH_3)_5NO]Cl_2$	402·0	n-C_5HuONO	403·7
$C_6H_5NH_2\cdot HCl$	401·4	$N_2H_6SO_4$	402·5
$K_3[Cr(CN)_5NO]$	400·7	$(CH_3)_3NO$	402·2
$[Rh(NH_3)_6](NO_3)_3$	400·7	NH_4NO_3	402·3
$[Ir(NH_3)_5Cl]Cl_2$	400·6	NH_4NO_3	407·2
		$(CH_3)_4NB_3H_8$	402·2
$N—N—B—(—N—N—)_3$	400·6	NH_3OHCl	402·1
$\dot{W}(CO)_2NO$		$(CONH_2)_2$	400·0
trans-$[Co(en)_2(NO_2)_2]$	400·4		
NO_3		$(NH_2)_2CNCN$	399·2
$[Rh(NH_3)_5NO_2]Br_2$	400·3		
$S_4N_4\cdot SbCl_5$	400·2	C_6H_5CN	398·4
S_7NH	400·2	C_5H_5N	398·0
$[Co(NH_3)_5NO]Cl_2$	400·2	$KSCN$	398·5
$Co(NH_3)_3(NO_2)_3$	400·2	$NH_3(s)$	398·8
$K[Co(NH_3)_2(NO_2)_4]$	400·0	S_4N_3Cl	399·6
$[Co(NH_3)_5NO_2]Cl_2$	400·0	NH_3SO_3	401·8
$[Co(NH_3)_6]_2(SO_4)_3$	400·0	$C_6H_5CONH_2$	399·4
$[Co(NH_3)_5Cl]Cl_2$	400·0	$(NPCl_2)_3$	399·5
trans-$[Co(NH_3)_4(NO_2)_2]$	399·9	$C_5H_5N\cdot HCl$	400·2
SO_4		BN	398·2
$[Cr(NH_3)_6]Cl_3$	399·9		
p-$NO_2C_6H_5CONH_2$	399·6	$Na_3(PO_2NH)_3$	398·5
$S_4N_4H_4$	399·5	$C_6H_5NH_2(g)$	405·5
$(NPCl_2)_4$	399·2	$NH_3(g)$	405·6
$K_3[Cr(CN)_6]$	398·6	$NNO(g)$	408·5
$K_3[Cr(CN)_5NO]$	398·4	$N_2(g)$	409·9

(continued overleaf)

†From ref. 2.12.   ‡Solid, unless otherwise indicated.

NITROGEN 1s (cont.)

Compound†	Binding energy (eV)	Compound	Binding energy (eV)
NO(g)	410·3	NO_2(g)	412·4
$C_6H_5NO_2$(g)	417·6	NNO(g)	412·5
P_3N_5	397·8	$(CH_3)_2NH$(g)	404·7
$K_4[Fe(CN)_6]·3H_2O$	397·6	CH_3NH_2(g)	405·3
VN	397·2	HCN(g)	406·8
CrN	396·6	N_2F_4(g)	412·4

†Solid, unless otherwise indicated.

XENON $3d_{5/2}$†

Compound‡	Binding energy (eV)
Xe	676·40
XeF_2	679·35
XeF_4	681·87
$XeOF_4$	683·42
XeF_6	684·28

†From ref. 2.37. ‡Gases.

SULPHUR 2p†

Compound‡	Binding energy (eV)
CS_2	169·8
H_2S	170·2
SO_2	174·8
SOF_2	176·2
SF_6	180·4

†From ref. 2.37. ‡Gases

IODINE—VARIOUS LEVELS†

Level	$2s_{1/2}$	$2p_{1/2}$	$2p_{3/2}$	$3d_{3/2}$	$3d_{5/2}$	$4s_{1/2}$	$4d_{3/2-5/2}$	
‡KI	5191·6	4856·2	4561·0	635·5	623·5	190·5	54·5	eV
‡KIO₃	5197·1	4861·9	4566·5	637·9	628·1	195·8	59·5	eV
‡KIO₄	5197·4	4861·7	4567·4	641·6	629·6	197·0	60·3	eV

†From ref. 2.12.   ‡Solid-state results.

OXYGEN 1s†

Compound‡	Binding energy (eV)
O_2	543·1
CH_3CHO	537·6
$C_2H_5C\overset{O}{\overset{\|}{}}OC_2H_5$	538·8
$CH_3C\overset{O}{\overset{\|}{}}OH$	538·2
C_2H_5OH	538·6
CH_3OH	538·9
$(CH_3)_2\,C{=}O$	539·0
$F_2S = O$	539·4
SO_2	539·6
H_2O	539·7
CH_3COOH	540·0
CO_2	540·8
N_2O	541·2
NO_2	541·3
CO	542·1
NO	543·3

†From ref. 2.37.   ‡Gases.

Binding Energies of Nitrogen Compounds†

Compound no.	Compound	(BE KNO₃) − (BE cmpd) (eV)	BE (eV)
1	Tetra-(n-butyl)ammonium bromide	6·2 ± 0·24	400·7
2	Tetraethylammonium bromide	6·2 ± 0·15	400·7
3	Tetraethylammonium chloride	5·8 ± 0·21	401·1
4	Tetraethylammonium perchlorate	6·4 ± 0·24	400·5
5	Tetramethylammonium tribromide	7·1 ± 0·11	399·8
6	Tetra-(n-propyl)ammonium hexafluorophosphate	5·8 ± 0·18	401·1
7	Tetraethylammonium borohydride	6·3 ± 0·21	400·6
8	Tetra-(n-propyl)ammonium borofluoride	6·5 ± 0·09	400·4
9	Tri-(n-propyl)amine hydro-hexafluoroarsenate	5·8 ± 0·11	401·1
10	Acetylcholine bromide	6·1 ± 0·11	400·8
11	Betaine	6·3 ± 0·24	400·6
12	Tetramethylammonium fluoride	5·7 ± 0·33	401·2
13	3-Chloroquinuclidine hydrochloride	6·8 ± 0·36	400·1
14	Trimethylphenylammonium bromide	6·2 ± 0·15	400·7
15	Tetraethylammonium p-toluenesulfonate	6·5 ± 0·11	400·4
16	N-ethylpyridinium bromide	6·2 ± 0·27	400·7
17	N-(n-butyl)pyridinium iodide	6·0 ± 0·11	400·9
18	N-(n-butyl)pyridinium bromide	6·3 ± 0·24	400·6
19	N-(n-butyl)-4-picolinium bromide	6·5 ± 0·11	400·4
20	N-ethyl-4-picolinium bromide	6·4 ± 0·13	400·5
21	N-ethyl-2-picolinium bromide	6·5 ± 0·15	400·4
22	N-ethyl-N-(n-butyl)-piperidinium	6·4 ± 0·27	400·5
23	N-ethyl-N-(n-butyl)-morpholinium bromide	6·5 ± 0·09	400·4
24	N-methyl-3-hydroxy-pyridinium chloride	6·6 ± 0·39	400·3
25	N-methyl-2-carboxy-pyridinium chloride	7·3 ± 0·24	399·6
26	N-methyl-3-carbomethoxy pyridinium iodide	6·5 ± 0·11	400·4
28	N-ethyl-4-carbomethoxy-pyridinium iodide	6·8 ± 0·25	400·1
29	N-methyl-4-picolinium iodide	6·5 ± 0·14	400·1

Compound no.	Compound	(BE KNO₃) − (BE cmpd) (eV)	BE (eV)
30	N-methyl-2-styrylpyridinium iodide	6·9 ± 0·15	400·0
31	N-methyl-2-(p-methoxy-styryl) pyridinium iodide	7·1 ± 0·20	399·8
32	N-(2-amidoethyl)-4-picolinium chloride	7·7 ± 0·16	399·2
		9·8 ± 0·18	397·1ᵇ
33	N-ethylquinolinium bromide	7·7 ± 0·17	399·2
34	N-(n-butyl)quinolinium bromide	7·6 ± 0·24	399·3
35	N-(n-butyl)quinolinium iodide	7·3 ± 0·21	399·6
36	N-(n-butyl)isoquinolinium bromide	7·0 ± 0·25	399·9
37	7-Methyl-dehydrobenzo-(a)quinolizinium bromide	7·8 ± 0·36	399·1
38	Dehydrobenzo(c)-quinolizinium chloride	8·1 ± 0·82	398·8
39	Dehydrobenzo(b)quinolizinium bromide	7·8 ± 0·37	399·1
40	Lucigenin nitrate	8·8 ± 0·23	398·1
		4·1 ± 0·15	402·8ᶜ
41	2,4-Dimethyl-3-ethyl-thiazolium iodide	6·8 ± 0·15	400·1
42	2,2,3,4-Tetramethyl-benzazolium iodide	6·5 ± 0·27	400·4
43	3-(2-Carboxyethyl)-2,5-dimethyl-benzoxazolium bromide	7·8 ± 0·28	399·1
46	N-(2,4-Dinitrophenyl)-pyridinium chloride	7·1 ± 0·24	399·8
		3·1ᵃ	403·8ᵈ
47	N-(n-butyl)-4-picolinium iodide	6·3 ± 0·24	400·7
49	N-methylacridinium chloride	7·7 ± 0·37	399·2
5	Acriflavin	9·7 ± 0·24	397·2
		11·3 ± 0·32	395·6ᵉ
51	Tetraethylammonium iodide	5·8 ± 0·06	401·1
52	Triethylamine hydrobromide	7·2 ± 0·25	399·7
53	Pyridine hydrobromide	7·6 ± 0·24	399·3
54	4-picoline hydrobromide	7·8 ± 0·16	399·1
55	Quinoline hydrobromide	8·4 ± 0·32	398·5
57	Acridine	11·8ᵃ	395·1
58	Sodium nitrate	−0·3	407·2
59	Potassium nitrate	0 ± 0·05	406·9
60	Tetramethylammonium bromide	6·2 ± 0·24	400·7

ᵃ Insufficient data for error estimate.   ᵇ Amide nitrogen.   ᶜ Nitrate nitrogen.   ᵈ Nitro nitrogen.   ᵉ Amino nitrogen.

† From ref. 6.8.

THE CALCULATION OF PARTIAL CHARGES ON ATOMS IN MOLECULES

The procedure for calculating partial charges on atoms in molecules according to the method of Pauling is quite straightforward. It is based on the following precepts:

(i) One unit of formal charge changes the electronegativity value of an element by approximately two-thirds of the electronegativity difference between that element and the next element in the periodic table.

(ii) The partial ionic character of a bond between A and B is given by $I = 1 - \exp [- 0.25 (\chi_A - \chi_B)^2]$ where χ_A and χ_B are the electronegativity of A and B respectively.

(iii) The sign of the partial charge is determined by the values of χ_A and χ_B being negative on the more electronegative atom or ion and positive on the more electropositive.

(iv) The total charge on an element, q, is the sum of the formal charge upon it, Q, and the partial ionic character, I, of all of the bonds in which the element is involved, i.e.

$$q = Q + \Sigma I.$$

(v) Only adjacent atoms are taken into account in the evaluation of q.

(vi) The contribution to q of a double or triple bond is taken to be twice or thrice that of the comparable single bond, e.g.

$$A{\equiv}B = 3(A{-}B); \ A{=}B = 2(A{-}B)$$

The application of these rules will now be illustrated by exemplary calculations. In accordance with the practice of Siegbahn, Pauling's original electronegativity values will be used.

(a) *Electronegativities of atoms being a formal charge*

Element	P		S		Cl
Electronegativity	2·1		2·5		3·0
(electronegativity difference)/3		0·13		0·17	
Element with formal charge		S^-		S^+	
Electronegativity	$(2·1 + 0·13) = 2·2$		$(3·0 - 0·17) = 2·8$		

This approach gives:

Element	H	C	C^-	N^-	N	N^+	O^-	O	S^-	S	S^+
Electronegativity	2·1	2·5	2·2	2·7	3·0	3·3	3·2	3·5	2·2	2·5	2·8

(b) *Partial ionic character, I*

$$\text{For N—C } I = 1 - \exp^- \left[\frac{(3·0 - 2·5)^2}{4} \right]$$

$$= 1 - \exp \ (-0·061) = 1 - 0·94$$

$$= 0·06.$$

N is more electronegative than C so when adding the contribution of the bond to get q_N add $-0·06$ and, conversely, add $+0·06$ when computing q_C.

$$\text{For } N^+\text{—S } I = 1 - \exp \left[\frac{- (3·3 - 2·5)^2}{4} \right]$$

$$= 0·13.$$

Since N^+ is more electronegative than S the contribution of the bond to q_N is $-0·13$ and to q_S is $+0·13$ even though there is a formal positive charge on the nitrogen.

This procedure has proved ineffective for N^+—H and a more realistic value has been calculated and used by Siegbahn. It and other values are collected together in tabular form below.

PARTIAL IONIC CHARACTER OF VARIOUS BONDS
(signs refer to charge on first listed element)

Bond	I	Bond	I	Bond	I
N—H	−0·18	S—O	+0·22	C—H	−0·04
N⁺—H	−0·30	S—O⁻	+0·11	C—O	+0·22
N—C	−0·06	S⁺—O	+0·12	C—O⁻	+0·11
N—C⁻	−0·15	S—C	0·00	C—N	+0·06
N⁺—C	−0·15	S⁻—C	+0·02	C⁻—N	+0·15
N⁺—N	−0·02	S⁺—C	−0·02		
		S⁺—N	+0·06	C—N⁺	+0·15
N⁺—N⁻	−0·09	S—N⁺	+0·15	C—S	0·00
N—O	+0·06			C—S⁻	−0·02
N—O⁻	+0·01	S—S⁻	−0·02	C—S⁺	+0·02
N⁺—O	+0·01			C—F	+0·43
N⁺—O⁻	0·0			C—Cl	+0·24
N—S	−0·06			C—Br	+ 0·17
N⁺—S	−0·15				

(c) *Calculation of q*

R is used throughout to indicate other parts of the molecule; since only adjacent atoms are taken into account the rest of the molecule is irrelevant.

(i)

on S $q = 2(+0·06) = +0·12.$

(ii)

on S $q = 0 \ (I_{S—S} = I_{S—C} = 0)$
on S⁻ $q = -1 + (+0·02) = -0·98 \ (Q = -1, I_{S⁻—C} = +0·02).$

(iii)

on S$^+$ $q = +1 + 3(-0\cdot02) + 2(+0\cdot12)$ $(Q = +1, 3S^+—C,$
$$2 S^+—O)$$
$$= +1\cdot18$$

(iv)

For the series the charge on both sulphur and oxygen atoms is computed:

q_{so_3} = $4(+0\cdot22)+0\cdot11$ = $4(+0\cdot22)+0\cdot11+(-0\cdot02)$
                                     = $2(+0\cdot22)+2(+0\cdot11)$
     $(= 4I_{s-o} + I_{s-o}-)$ $(= 4I_{s-o} + I_{s-o}- + I_{s-s}-)$ $(= 2I_{s-o} + 2I_{s-o}-)$
     = $+0\cdot99$ = $+0\cdot97$ = $+0\cdot66$
q_s = 0   = $-1 + (0\cdot02)$ = 0
                   = $-0\cdot98$

$$q_0 = \frac{-1 + (-0\cdot99)}{3} \qquad = \frac{-2 + (-0\cdot97)}{3} \qquad = \frac{-2 + (-0\cdot066)}{3}$$
$$= -0\cdot67 \qquad\qquad = -0\cdot99 \qquad\qquad = -0\cdot89$$

The charge on the oxygens must be equal and opposite to that on the sulphur in the SO_3 group. The charge is averaged over the three oxygen atoms.

(v) The partial charge on an atom within a molecule which has several resonance structures will vary with the structure.

The charge on nitrogen is

for I $q = 2(-0\cdot18) + (-0\cdot06) = -0\cdot42$ (2N—H, 1N—C)
for II $q = +1 + 2(-0\cdot30) + 2(-0\cdot15) = +0\cdot10$ $(Q = +1$
2N$^+$—H, 2N$^+$—C)

The charge corresponding to the experimentally found chemical shift is -0.14 so it is deduced that the weighting of I: II is $54:46$.

REFERENCE

R. NORDBERG, R. G. ALBRIDGE, T. BERGMARK, V. ERICSON, J. HEDMAN, C. NORDLING, K. SIEGBAHN and B. J. LINDBERG, *Arkiv Kemi.*, 1968, **28**, 257.

APPENDIX 6

PROBABILITY OF AUGER TRANSITION AS A FUNCTION OF ATOMIC NUMBER

Z	10	15	20	25	30	35	40	45	50	55	60	65	70
P	0·99	0·95	0·86	0·71	0·55	0·43	0·31	0·22	0·16	0·13	0·11	0·09	0·07

The fractional energy carried off by X-ray emission is $1 - P$.

INDEX

Note: U = UV-PES, X = X-ray PES

OTHER TITLES IN THE SERIES IN ANALYTICAL CHEMISTRY